D1441904

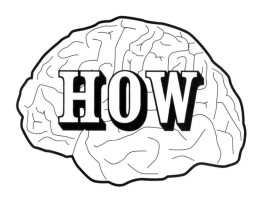

1000 COMPELLING ANSWERS TO 1000 INTRIGUING 'HOW?' QUESTIONS.
TRIVIA TO ENLIGHTEN AND EDUCATE.

Managing Editor: Simon Melhuish
Series Editor: Nikole G Bamford
Designer: Stephen Godson
Cover: Alan Shiner

Published by
The Lagoon Group
PO Box 311, KT2 5QW, UK
PO Box 990676, Boston, MA 02199, USA

ISBN: 1905439741
© LAGOON BOOKS 2006

www.thelagoongroup.com

Printed in China

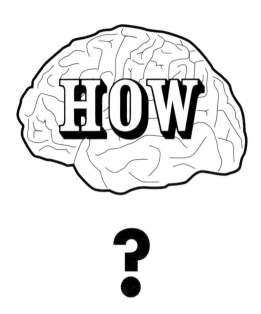

1000 COMPELLING ANSWERS TO 1000 INTRIGUING 'HOW?' QUESTIONS.
TRIVIA TO ENLIGHTEN AND EDUCATE.

How many languages have J.K. Rowling's Harry Potter books been published in?

61 languages.

How is a bacterian camel different from a dromedary?

A dromedary has only one hump and is widely known as a racing camel. The sport is particularly popular in the United Arab Emirates.

How long is the longest river on earth?

At 4,160 miles (6695km), the Nile, in North Africa, is the longest river. The second longest river is the Amazon which winds through much of South America for approximately 4,000 miles (6437km). The third is the Yangtze in Asia with a length of 3,900 miles (6276km).

How would you find a needle in a haystack?

With a magnet!

How big was the biggest pearl ever found?

The Pearl of Allah, as it is known, was found in the Philippines in 1934. It weighed 6.3 kg (14 lbs 2 oz).

How long can an elephant's tusk grow?
Up to 11.5ft/3.5 meters in length.

How many presidents shared a name with an automobile?
Two — Gerald Ford and Abraham Lincoln.

How many US presidents have died in office?
Eight:

William Harrison (1841)
Zachary Taylor (1850)
Abraham Lincoln (1865)
James A. Garfield (1881)
William McKinley (1901)
Warren Harding (1923)
Franklin D. Roosevelt (1945)
John F. Kennedy (1963)

How many US Presidents died of natural causes while in office?
Four:

William Harrison (1841)
Zachary Taylor (1850)
Warren Harding (1923)
Franklin D. Roosevelt (1945)

How many loaves make up a bakers' dozen?

Thirteen — also know as a long dozen. One of the earliest uses of the expression was in 13th century England where 13 loaves were sold for the price of 12 to safeguard against being accused of short-changing customers. The practice made sense given that the punishment for cheating customers was to have a hand chopped off with an axe.

How many US Presidents were shot while in office?

Six:

Andrew Jackson (1835) He survived.
Abraham Lincoln (1865)
James A. Garfield (1881)
William McKinley (1901)
John F. Kennedy (1963)
Ronald Reagan (1981) He survived.

How does a three-toed sloth differ from a two-toed sloth?

Obviously the three-toed sloth has an extra toe on its forelimb. The other principal difference is that a three-toed sloth has a tail; the two-toed sloth doesn't.

How many of the world's ten highest peaks are to be found in the Himalayas?

Nine — K2, the second highest peak, is located in the Karakorum Mountain Range in territory disputed by China, Pakistan and China.

How does Chinese long soup differ from short soup?

Short soup has wontons, or small dumplings, in it. Long soup is made with noodles.

How fast can an ostrich run?

45 mph/72kph.

How fast does a peregrine falcon swoop on its prey?

It is thought that falcons can travel at more than 100 miles per hour (160kph). It has also been estimated that speeds approaching 200 mph (320kph) have been reached but this is difficult to judge accurately.

How many sportsmen from how many nations took part in the first modern Olympics in 1896?

245 athletes from 15 countries.

How many kinds of deadly snakes are there in the United States?

Four:

The rattlesnake
The coral snake
The copperhead
The cottonmouth water moccasin

How long was the 100 Years War?

118 years. Primarily a long period of battles between France and England, the first of which took place in 1337, the last in 1453.

How long is the Great Wall of China?

6,700 kilometers (4,163 miles) from the east to the west of China.

How many floors are there in the Empire State Building?

103.

How many strings are there on a Stradivarius?

The most famous of all violins has, like other violins, four strings.

How wide is the Grand Canyon at its widest point?

18 miles/29 km.

How many stars were there on the first official US flag?

13 stars

How many athletes, to date, have run world records in under ten seconds for the 100 meters since electronic timing was introduced?

Eight — Carl Lewis and Leroy Burrell broke the record twice.

Jim Hines (USA) — 9.95, 1968
Calvin Smith (USA) — 9.93, 1983
Carl Lewis (USA) — 9.92, 1987
Leroy Burrell (USA) — 9.90, 1991
Carl Lewis (USA) — 9.86, 1991
Leroy Burrell (USA) — 9.85, 1994
Donovan Bailey (Canada) — 9.84, 1996
Maurice Greene (USA) — 9.79, 1999
Asafa Powell (Jamaica) — 9.77, 2005
Justin Gatlin (USA) — 9.77, 2006

Ben Johnson's time of 9.83 and Tim Montgomery's time of 9.78 were struck from the records because of drug use.

How far is it to the moon?

The distance varies according to the moon's orbit but, on average, the distance is 238,900 miles (384,402 km).

How long did it take to play the longest world championship chess match?

The match between Karpov and Kasparov in 1984/85 lasted 48 games and 159 days. The match was abandoned and a rematch ordered.

How many moons or satellites orbit the planet Neptune?

At least 13, but it may have more that are so small they haven't been discovered yet.

Naiad

Thalassa

Despina

Galatea

Larissa

Proteus

Triton

Nereid

S/2002 N1

S/2002 N2

S/2002 N3

S/2002 N4

S/2003 N1

How can Eva Longoria, of Desperate Housewives fame, be seen from space?

In April 2006, to celebrate the 100th issue of Maxim Magazine, a mock-up of the cover was erected on the California-Nevada border. It measured 100ft x 75ft and featured Eva Longoria. And, apparently, she can be seen from space.

How many years was Elaine Esposito — known as the real-life Sleeping Beauty — in a coma?

37 years and 111 days. She went into the hospital for a simple operation on August 1941 and stayed in a coma for the rest of her life. She died on November 26, 1978.

How many times did Sean Connery star as James Bond?

Seven:

Dr No (1962)

From Russia With Love (1963)

Goldfinger (1964)

Thunderball (1965)

You Only Live Twice (1967)

Diamonds Are Forever (1971)

Never Say Never Again (1983)

How many countries does the comic strip Garfield appear in?

111.

How long can an elephant live?

Elephants can live to about 70 years of age.

How do elephants sleep?

Standing up.

How does an African elephant differ from an Indian elephant?

An Indian elephant has much smaller ears than its African counterpart.

How old was Sleeping Beauty when she pricked her finger on a spindle and fell asleep because of a fairy's curse?

Sixteen.

How deep is the ocean?

The deepest known point in the ocean is the Challenger Deep, in the Pacific Ocean, near Guam. It is 35,797 feet (10,911 meters) deep.

How many oceans are there on the planet?

Four:

Pacific, Atlantic, Arctic, Indian

Some think the waters surrounding Antarctica, i.e. the Southern Ocean, should also be included.

How long is the longest straight line of railway?

The Trans-Australian railway across the Nullarbor Plain between Nurina in West Australia and Watson in South Australia runs for 309 miles (497 km) without a curve.

How many countries have played in all 18 World Cup soccer tournaments since the contest began in 1930?

One — Brazil.

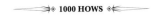

How many reindeer pull Father Christmas's sleigh?
Nine:
Rudolph, Dasher, Dancer, Prancer, Vixen, Donder (or Donner), Blitzen, Cupid, Comet.

How many stripes are there on the current American flag?
There are 13 horizontal stripes, representing the original 13 colonies.

How was Alexander the Great's body preserved?
It was stored in a jar of honey.

How long was Cypriot Kively Papajohn, 76 years old, stuck in an elevator for?
On December 28, 1987, Kively came home from grocery shopping and the lift stopped. On January 2 1988, six days after it all started, she finally got out, setting the record for the world's longest time trapped in elevator. Probably without the groceries 'though.

How many steps are there to the top of the Eiffel Tower?
1652.

How often is the Eiffel Tower painted?

Once every seven years; it takes nearly 50 tons of paint to spruce it up.

How long did it take the record-breaking Concorde to fly around the world?

31 hrs, 27 minutes and 49 seconds.

How many stars are there on the Australian flag?

Six. The seven-pointed star below the Union Jack represents the six states plus Australia's territories. The five stars of the Southern Cross is a constellation that can be seen from all Australian states and territories.

How many Pharaohs were buried in Egypt's Valley of the Kings?

62 tombs have been discovered, from a simple pit to a tomb with over 120 chambers and corridors.

How far can a flea jump?

The longest measured distance is 13 inches (32.5cm).

How long is the longest feature film title?

With 168 characters in the title:

Night of the Day of the Dawn of the Son of the Bride of the Return of the Revenge of the Terror of the Attack of the Evil, Mutant Alien, Flesh Eating, Hellbound, Zombified Living Dead Part 2: In Shocking 2-D. (1991) The 2005 follow-up was not quite as long: Night of the Day of the Dawn of the Son of the Bride of the Return of the Revenge of the Terror of the Attack of the Evil, Mutant, Hellbound, Flesh-Eating, Subhumanoid, Zombified Living Dead Part 3.

Another killer title is The Persecution and Assassination of Jean-Paul Marat as Performed by the Inmates of the Asylum of Charenton Under the Direction of the Marquis de Sade (1967). In the US the film was released as Marat/Sade..

How fast is the fastest animal?

A cheetah can run at 65 mph/105kph.

How does the iguana species of lizard communicate?

It does push-ups and other kinds of body pumping.

How long was Charlton Heston trapped in Peking in the 1963 film?

55 days in Peking.

How many actors have played Inspector Clouseau in the Pink Panther films?

Four:

Alan Arkin appeared in Inspector Clouseau (1968)

Tedd Wass appeared in Curse of the Pink Panther (1983)

Steve Martin appeared in The Pink Panther (2006)

Peter Sellers played the part 6 times in:

The Pink Panther:

A Shot in the Dark

The Return of the Pink Panther

The Pink Panther Strikes Again

Revenge of the Pink Panther

The Trail of the Pink Panther

The Trail of the Pink Panther was completed after Peter Sellers' death and his appearance in the film is made by using unused clips and out-takes from earlier Pink Panther films. Roberto Benigni played Clouseau's son in Son of the Pink Panther (1993)

How long does a koala sleep during a 24-hour period?

Between 18 and 22 hours.

How much was paid for the world's most expensive car in 1990?

Between 1927 and 1933, Bugatti built six Type 41 Royale cars. In 1990, one of them was sold in Japan for 15 million US dollars.

How similar is an orangutan to a human being?

About 97 percent of an orangutan's genetic makeup is the same as humans.

How would the phrase My Very Excellent Mother Just Sent Us Nine Pizzas help an astronomy student?

The first letter of each word starts the name of a planet in order of proximity to the sun.

Mercury

Venus

Earth

Mars

Jupiter

Saturn

Uranus

Neptune

Pluto (although now declared as a dwarf planet)

How loud is the loudest snore on record?

93 decibels. That's louder than the sound made by a doorbell.

How many puppets were used for the Broadway version of Disney's The Lion King?

More than 232.

How long does it take light to travel from the sun to the earth?
8.3 minutes.

How long was the shortest reign by a pope?
13 days by Pope Urban VII in September of 1850.

How did the Gossamer Albatross cross the English Channel?
Pedal power. The amateur cyclist Bryan Allen turned a large two-bladed propeller by pedaling as hard as he could across the Channel from England to France.

How long was the longest reign by a pope?
Pope Pius IX reigned for 31 years, 7 months and 23 days from 1846 to 1878.

How many Oscars did Lord of the Rings: The Return of the King win?
11. It is the only film to win all the awards in all the categories in which it was nominated. Other films to win 11 Oscars were Ben Hur (with 12 nominations) and Titanic (14 nominations).

How much of the world's gas (petrol) does the US consume?
40%.

How many letters are in the world's longest alphabet?
The Cambodian alphabet contains 74 letters. The Chinese language contains over 5000 symbols which are generally regarded not to constitute an alphabet.

How many letters are there in the world's shortest alphabet?
Rotokas, which is the native language of the Solomon Islands, has only 11 letters.

How many years difference was there between Anna Nicole Smith and J. Howard Marshall when they married?
63. She was 26 and he was 89.

How long did the funniest marriage in Hollywood last?
Bob Hope was married to his wife Dolores for 69 years, until the comedian's death in 2003.

How long was Britney Spears married to Jason Alexander?

55 hours.

How many men did Elizabeth Taylor marry?

Seven:

  Conrad Hilton Jr.

  Michael Wilding

  Michael Todd

  Eddie Fisher

  Richard Burton (twice)

  Senator John Warner

  Larry Fortensky

How do dolphins sleep without drowning?

Only a half of a dolphin's brain goes to sleep. The awake half takes care of breathing and swimming.

How many goals did Diego Maradona score in Argentina's 1986 World Cup campaign?

Five — two of which he scored against England. One of those was the infamous 'hand of God' goal where he blatantly used his hand to control the ball before scoring.

How long does the world's largest moth, the Atlas, live?

One day. In that day it will emerge from a cocoon, find a mate, lay eggs and then die.

How many of Jules Verne's fifty-four novels have a number in the title?

Ten:

Five Weeks in a Balloon

Paris in the 20th Century

20,000 Leagues Under the Sea

The Adventures of Three Englishmen and Three Russians in South Africa

Around the World in Eighty Days

A Captain at Fifteen

The Begum's Millions

Eight Hundred Leagues on the Amazon

Ticket No. 9672

Two Years' Vacation

How many players are there in a lacrosse team?

Ten — one goalkeeper, three defenders, three midfielders and three attackers.

How many furlongs are there in a mile?

Eight.

How does the Manx cat differ from most other felines?
It has no tail.

How blind is a bat?
Bats are not blind. They have small eyes which are sensitive to light.

How many species of bats are there?
More than 1000.

How do bats differ from other mammals?
They are the only mammals truly able to fly.

How is it that ladybugs are only seen in summer?
They hibernate in winter.

How many players are in a Rugby Union team?
Fifteen.

How many players make up a Rugby League team?
Thirteen.

How many cats are thought to be kept as pets worldwide?
Between 63 and 65 million.

How many symbols are there on a deck of cards?
364.

How many times has Germany won football's World Cup?
Three times.

How many times has Brazil won the Football World Cup?
Five — in 1958, 1962, 1970, 1994 and 2002.

How many World Cups did Pelé help Brazil to win?
Three — 1958, 1962 and 1970.

How far does the Arctic tern migrate every year?
22,000 miles. From the Artic Circle to Antarctica and back again.

How long does it take the moon to orbit the earth?
27.5 earth days, although from new moon to new moon the duration is 29.5 days.

How many Academy Awards did Katherine Hepburn win?
Four. She won Best Actress Oscars for Morning Glory, Guess Who's Coming to Dinner?, The Lion in Winter and On Golden Pond.

How far was the longest fall down stairs?
In a charity event to raise money, stunt man Martin Shenton deliberately threw himself down 109 stairs at the Ashton Memorial in Lancaster, England. No bones were broken.

How long can a person survive without a heartbeat?
Julie Mills underwent an operation for a heart infection in an Oxford (UK) Hospital in 1998. For six days she was attached to an electric pump which pumped blood round her body. For those six days she had no heartbeat. When her infection was cured, her heart started beating of its own accord.

How many steps are there on the longest spiral staircase?

At the White County LLC Pattiki Mine, in Illinois, the spiral staircase is 1,103 feet (336 meters) deep and has 1,520 steps.

How many steps are there in the longest staircase?

The Niesen funicular in Switzerland climbs to an altitude of 7,661 feet (2,335 meters). Beside the tramway is a service staircase which has 11,674 steps.

How long is the world's longest railway?

The Trans-Siberian Railway runs from Moscow to Vladivostok — a journey of slightly more than 6,000 miles (10,000 km).

How cold does it get in Antarctica?

The coldest report temperature was -89.4 C or -129 degrees F.

How long is the longest record for most consecutive rainy days?

A ranch in Oahu, Hawaii reported 247 rainy days in a row between August 27, 1993 and April 30, 1994.

How long was the longest Slinky in the world?

71 feet (21 meters). It was made from 34 Slinkys soldered together.

How long was the longest-recorded length of a snake?

32 feet, 9.5in (10meters). It was a reticulated python, found in Indonesia in 1912.

How many 'gifts' were given during the twelve days of Christmas, according to the song?

364:

  Twelve drummers drumming

  Eleven pipers piping

  Ten lords a-leaping

  Nine ladies dancing

  Eight maids a-milking

  Seven swans a-swimming

  Six geese a-laying

  Five golden rings

  Four calling birds

  Three French hens

  Two turtle doves

  And a partridge in a pear tree!

How many people perished when the Titanic sank?

1523.

How many pounds of ham were on the Titanic when it sunk?
7,500.

How heavy was one link on the anchor chain of the Titanic?
About 175 lbs.

How many dogs survived the sinking of the Titanic?
Two.

**How many cigars were loaded onto the Titanic before
she left on her maiden voyage?**
8,000.

How big is the tip of an iceberg?
It is a fifth to a seventh of its overall size.

How long did 1969's 'giant leap for mankind' take?
Neil Armstrong and Buzz Aldrin spent two and half hours on the surface of the moon.

How many countries have a border with Russia?
14: North Korea, China, Mongolia, Kazakhstan, Azerbaijan, Georgia, Ukraine, Belarus, Latvia, Estonia, Finland, Norway, Lithuania and Poland. The Russian border stretches for more than 57,000 km (35,418 miles).

How long was the world's longest engagement?
67 years — Octavio Guillen and Adriana Martinez were engaged in 1902 and finally married in 1969. They were fifteen when they were engaged and 82 when they married.

How many languages are spoken on earth?
Estimates of 'living languages,' i.e. those currently in use, vary but by all accounts the number exceeds 6,000. One estimate suggests that as many as 6,912 different languages are in use.

How many words make up the longest album title by a recent recording artist?
90 words — Fiona Apple's album is called: When the Pawn Hits the Conflicts He Thinks Like a King What He Knows Throws the Blows When He Goes to the Fight and He'll Win the Whole Thing 'Fore He Enters the Ring There's No Body to Batter When Your Mind Is Your Might So When You Go Solo, You Hold Your Own Hand and Remember That Depth Is the Greatest of Heights and If You Know Where You Stand, Then You Know Where To Land and If You Fall It Won't Matter, Cuz You'll Know That You're Right.

How long did Italian fans of Monty Python's Life of Brian (1979) have to wait to see the film?

11 years — the film was not released in Italy until 1990. The film was not shown in the Channel Island of Jersey until 2001 and then only with an adults only rating.

How many inches is the longest recorded beard on a woman?

Vivian Wheeler of Illinois has the longest beard at 11 inches (27.9 cm) and still growing.

How do you solve a problem like Maria?

In The Sound of Music, Maria was sent from her convent to be governess to the Von Trapp children.

How long is the longest annual foot race?

3,100 miles (4,989km) — it is called the Self-Transcendence Race and is run by the Sri Chinmoy Marathon team.

How far was the longest human cannonball flight?

Dave 'Cannonball' Smith Sr. was shot 185 ft 10 inches/56.54 meters in Pennsylvania in 1998.

How long was the longest ever applause for a performance?

After appearing in the Moor of Venice at Vienna on July 30, 1991, Placido Domingo was given 101 curtain calls and 80 minutes of clapping. Bravo!

How long was the longest Lego structure ever built?

A millipede stretching for 1,052 meters or 3,451 feet was built by children in Bangkok in 2003. They used 2,477,140 bricks.

How long was the world's longest baseball throw?

The longest known measured throw was by the Canadian minor league pitcher Glen Corbous who, after a running start, threw the ball 445 feet and 10 inches/53.5m way back in 1957.

How long was the longest crocodile ever caught?

20.3 ft/6m — caught off the coast of Australia.

How long was the longest moonwalk?

Alan Shepherd and Edgar Mitchell each spent 9 hours on the moon when Apollo 14 landed there in 1971.

How long was the prison sentence given to Gabriel Grandos for failing to deliver 42,768 letters?

In 1972 this postman was sentenced to 7,109 years behind bars. The prosecution had requested a lot longer.

How long was the longest boxing match?

7 hours and 19 minutes — the bout took place between Andy Bowen and Jack Burke in New Orleans in1893. Exhaustion forced the end to the match. The result was declared a draw.

How long did the longest lasting known sneezing fit last?

978 days — Donna Griffiths started sneezing on January 13, 1981 and didn't stop until September 16, 1983. That's no sneezing matter!

How many times does the word God appear in the St James version of the Bible?

4444 times.

How many avenues radiate from the Arc de Triomphe in Paris?

12.

How many wives did Henry the Eighth have?
Six:
  Catherine of Aragon
  Anne Boleyn
  Jane Seymour
  Anne of Cleves
  Catherine Howard
  Catherine Parr

How long is the longest insect?
A walking stick or phasmida has been measured at 555mm, just less than 22 inches.

How long is the world's longest country?
Chile stretches for 2,700 miles/4,300 km.

How many wives did Henry the Eighth have beheaded?
Two — Anne Boleyn and Catherine Howard.

How long is a round in boxing?
3 minutes.

How many ways are there to win a boxing match?

Five:

Knockout

Technical Knockout

Disqualification

    (like when Mike Tyson bit off a piece of Evander Holyfield's ear during their 1997 fight)

On Points

When the opponent retires or 'throws in the towel'

How many eyes are in a pack of 52 cards?

42.

How many months have 31 days?

Seven:

January

March

May

July

August

October

December

How many colored balls are there in billiards?

15.

How many lanes are used in Olympic swimming races?

Eight.

How far is one lap of an Olympic swimming pool?

50 meters.

How long is the longest competitive swimming race in the Olympics?

1500 meters.

How many squares are there on a chessboard?

64.

How many dots would you have in your hand if you were about to throw two dice?

42.

How does the puffer fish avoid being a fish dinner?

It fills itself with water and becomes too big for other fish to swallow.

How much does a liter of water weigh?
1kg.

How many legs does a spider have?
Eight.

How many wings does a bee have?
Four.

How many eyes does a bee have?
Five.

How many flowers must bees tap to make one pound of honey?
About two million.

How long is a newborn Kangaroo?
About an inch (2.54cm) long.

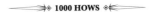

How far can a fully-grown kangaroo hop?
30ft/9m.

How much milk can a cow produce during its lifetime?
200,000 glasses of milk.

How many times can a woodpecker peck per second?
Up to 20 times.

How many eyelids does a camel have?
Three on each eye — for extra protection against sand storms.

How shocking is an electric eel?
An eel can produce a shock of up to 650 volts.

How can you tell the difference between a wild turkey and a domesticated turkey?
A wild turkey can fly whereas a farm-bred turkey cannot.

How many fingers did Anne Boleyn have?

11, including thumbs. It has been said that Anne was born with six fingers on one hand. As this was thought to be a sign of the devil it is highly strange that Henry the Eighth married her.

How many rounds are there in a championship boxing match?

12.

How high was the tallest vertical candle?

In 2005 a British candle company made a candle that was 83.5ft/25.3m high

How long did the longest dance marathon last?

5,152 hours and 48 minutes — Mike Ritof and Edith Bourdreaux started dancing in August 29, 1930 at the Merry Garden Ballroom in Chicago and didn't stop until April 1, 1931. Their prize was $2,000.

How long do scientists think was the length of the longest dinosaur?

The Seismosaurus is estimated to have been about 150ft/45.5m long and weighed between 80 and 100 tons.

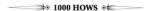

How long did the longest recorded fit of hiccups last?

68 years — Charles Osborne of Iowa started to hiccup in 1922 and stopped in 1990. Throughout, he led a normal life, marrying and having 8 children. At worst he hiccupped 40 times a minute. Towards the end of the bout he hiccupped 20 times a minute.

How many stories did Betty Lou Oliver fall in an elevator when a bomber crashed into the Empire State Building in 1945?

75 stories — about 1,000 feet/over 300m. And she survived.

How long is the longest lake on earth?

Lake Tanganyika, which runs through Congo and Tanzania, is 420 miles/676 km long.

How far did someone fall and survive?

In 1972 the plane in which Vesna Vulovic was flying, exploded. She fell 33,300 ft/10,150m into snow and survived.

How long is the world's longest fence?

3,509 miles/5,614km — the fence which runs from Jimbour in Queensland south to the great Australia Bight was built to keep rabbits out of farmland.

How is Oprah Noodlemantra better known?

Johnny Depp — on the credits of Nightmare on Elm Street 6: Freddy's Dead: The Final Nightmare his character was listed as being played by Oprah Noodlemantra.

How long was the world's longest gold chain?

The chain was made for the jewelers AngloGold and was 2.5 miles/4.1 km long and weighed 200 kilos. It was portioned off and sold in Dubai.

How long are the longest hands?

From wrist to the tip of his middle finger Hussain Bisad holds the record with a measurement of 10.59 inches (26.9cm). As he is over 7.8ft/2.3m tall he also has very large feet.

How long can hairs on a human leg grow?

The current record is held by Tim Stinton of Australia — 4.88in/12.4cm. No need for leg warmers then.

How far can a mole tunnel in a day?

300ft/91m.

How many sides does a snowflake have?

They are hexagonal — having six sides.

How big was the largest recorded snowflake?

15in x 8in/38cm by 20cm. It fell at Fort Keogh, Montana back in 1887.

How long can a hummingbird hover in the one place?

Up to an hour.

How many teeth does a mosquito have?

47.

How many teeth does a snail have?

About 15,000, arranged in rows on its tongue.

How far can a champagne cork fly after exploding from a bottle?

The longest known flight was in 1988 — 177 feet and 9 inches/64.6m.

How tall are the tallest trees?
The Pacific Coast Redwoods are over 300ft/91m tall.

How tall is a giraffe at birth?
They can be born up to 6 feet (nearly 2 meters) in length.

How does a male giraffe prove his masculinity?
He neck wrestles any opponent giraffe.

How tall can a giraffe grow?
Up to 19ft/5.75m tall. It is the world's tallest animal.

How many breeds of dog have blue tongues?
Two — the Chow Chow and Chinese Shar-Pei.

How many species of frogs are there?
Over 2,600 — they can be found everywhere except Antarctica.

How do chimpanzees ward off their enemies?
They use large sticks and branches as clubs, beating them or
throwing them at approaching predators or humans.

How did the famous warrior Attila the Hun die?
He bled to death from a nosebleed on his wedding night.

How far can a lion's roar reach?
It can be heard about 5 miles/8 km away.

How do you treat wasp and bee stings?
Put vinegar on wasp stings and bicarbonate of soda on bee stings.

How long is a chameleon's tongue?
Twice the length of its body.

How unlucky was the elephant in Berlin zoo during World War II?
It was killed by the very first bomb dropped on Berlin by the Allies.

How is a cappella music performed?

With just voice(s) — no musical accompaniment.

How did the kit company Airfix start out?

By making combs.

How long has the Oprah Winfrey Show been a worldwide phenomenon?

The first Oprah show was broadcast nationwide on September 8, 1986.

How many post-war Ealing Comedies were made?

Nine:

Hue and Cry (1946)

King Hearts and Coronets (1949)

Passport to Pimlico (1949)

Whisky Galore! (1949)

The Lavender Hill Mob (1951)

The Man in the White Suit (1951)

The Titfield Thunderbolt (1953)

The Maggie (1954)

The Ladykillers (1955)

How many characters did Alec Guinness play in Kind Hearts and Coronets?

Eight:

Duke Etherel

The Banker

Reverend Lord Henry d'Ascoyne

General Lord Rufus D'Ascoyne

Admiral Horatio d'Ascoyne

Young Henry d'Ascoyne

Lady Agatha d'Ascoyne

Lord Ascoyne d'Ascoyne

How did Johnny Depp find inspiration for his character, Captain Jack Sparrow, in the Pirates of the Caribbean movies?

By watching the Rolling Stones — Keith Richard in particular.

How is Rebecca Rolfe better known?

Pocahontas.

How did Pocahontas die?

She died of smallpox while in London.

How many characters did Peter Sellers play in Dr. Strangelove or: How I Stopped Worrying and Learned to Love the Bomb (1964)?

Three:

  Group Captain Lionel Mandrake

  President Merkin Muffley

  Dr Strangelove

How long was Nelson Mandela imprisoned on Robben Island?

27 years.

How did Raquel Welch make a Fantastic Voyage in 1966?

She was inside a miniaturized submarine that was injected into the bloodstream of a dying diplomat.

How many times has King Kong left the ladies screaming?

Three — the first time he encountered a damsel in distress, played by Fay Wray, was in the original movie, made in 1933. Jessica Lange played the part in the 1976 version of the film. Naomi Watts was the female lead in 2005.

How was Pocahontas commemorated in 1875?

She appeared on the back of a US $20 bill.

How did some Native Americans make use of the beaver's ability to gnaw through trees?
They used beaver teeth as knives because they are incredibly sharp.

How did Margaret Mitchell, the author of Gone with the Wind, die?
She was hit by a cab while crossing the road.

How many actors have refused an Oscar?
Two — George C. Scott refused the Oscar for Patton (1970) and Marlon Brando refused the Oscar for his role in The Godfather (1972). Back in 1935 the writer Dudley Nichols refused to accept an Oscar for his movie The Informer because the Writer's Guild was on strike against the studios at the time.

How many novels did Margaret Mitchell publish in her lifetime?
Only one — Gone With the Wind.

How did the Russian mystic Rasputin die?
He was poisoned with cyanide, shot three times, then thrown into a river.

How does a boa constrictor kill?

It squeezes its prey until it dies.

How many rainy days are meant to follow if it rains on St. Swithin's Day?

40.

How did the Greek playwright Aeschylus die?

Supposedly he was killed by a tortoise that was dropped on his head by an eagle which mistook his bald head for a rock. Eagles used rocks to crack open tortoises so they could eat them.

How is Ceylon now known?

Sri Lanka.

How long does the Le Mans car endurance race last?

24 hours.

How did Wild Bill Hickok die?

He was shot in the back of the head while playing poker.

How did Jim Fixx die?

The publicist for jogging died of a heart attack, while jogging.

How many presidents are commemorated at Mount Rushmore?

Four:

  George Washington
  Thomas Jefferson
  Abraham Lincoln
  Theodore Roosevelt

How did Al Capone describe the business he was in?

On his business cards he described himself as a second-hand furniture dealer from Chicago.

How much did the United States pay Russia for Alaska in 1867?

7.2 million dollars. That's about 2 cents an acre.

How many teeth does an adult dog have?
42.

How many states are there in the United Arab Emirates?
Seven:
  Abu Zaby
  'Ajman, Al Fujayrah
  Ash Shariqua
  Dubayy
  Umm al Quaywayn
  Ra's al Khaymah

How many kinds of kangaroos are there?
More than 50.

How many US Presidents died in the White House?
Two — William Harrison (1841) and Zachary Taylor (1850).

How many US Presidents are buried in Washington?
One — Woodrow Wilson is buried in the Washington Cathedral.

How many teeth can a shark grow in its lifetime?
Up to 20,000.

How old is Peter Pan?
Peter Pan is 'the boy who never grew up' so we don't know exactly how old he is. His first appearance in print was in the J.M. Barrie book The Little White Bird in 1902.

How many times does a hummingbird's heart beat per minute?
On average 1,260 times a minute. It has the most rapid metabolism of any bird.

How many times does a human heart beat per minute?
60–80 times.

How many times does an elephant's heart beat per minute?
28.

How many times a minute does a blue whale's heart beat?
Nine.

How long can a cockroach live without its head before starving to death?

Nine days.

How long does the Muslim festival of Ramadan last?

One lunar month.

How are Mizaru, Mikazaru and Mazaru more commonly known?

They are the three wise monkeys, See no evil, Hear no evil and Speak no evil.

How long does the Jewish festival of Chanukah last?

Eight days and nights.

How does Santa Claus get around in Finland?

According to Finnish folklore, he leaves his sleigh behind and rides on a goat named Ukko.

How are bad kids punished by Santa Claus in Holland?

According to Dutch folklore, they are put in a bag and taken to Spain.

How did the White House become white?

The president's residence was built of sandstone which is very porous and subject to extensive water damage. To protect the building, it was sealed with a mixture of salt, rice and glue, giving it its first distinctive white coat.

How many eyes does a butterfly have?

12,000.

How many miles of blood vessels are there in the human body?

Laid end to end they would stretch about 60,000 miles/96,000 km.

How many vocal sounds can a cat make?

Over a hundred.

How many vocal sounds can a dog make?

About ten.

How long is a moment?

It is defined as one and a half minutes, according to Old English time measurements.

How much blood does the average heart pump in a lifetime?
The equivalent of filling one hundred average swimming pools.

How many credit cards were issued to the first ever customers to use them?
In 1951 Diners Club issued 200 cards to its customers, who could use them in 27 New York restaurants.

How many hairs cover the human head?
About 100,000.

How many brain cells does the average brain contain?
About 100 billion before the rot sets in.

How many viruses can cause the common cold?
Any one of 1,000 viruses can set noses running.

How much of the earth's water is salty?
97.2%.

How old was the oldest lobster found to be?
50.

How long has the rapid home pregnancy test been available?
Since 1985.

How many colors can the human eye see?
250 different pure colors, 17,000 mixed colors and 300 shades of grey.

How many colors can a bee see?
Green, blue and ultra-violet. It sees red as black.

How many bones is a baby born with?
About 350.

How many bones does an adult have?
206.

How far can a flying fish travel?
It can leap up to 20ft/6m out of the water and glide for about 660ft/200 meters.

How many people are left handed?
About 12%.

How many people travel by air every year?
About one billion people take plane journeys every year.

How many commercial airplanes crash every year?
On average about 40.

How much garbage do Americans make every year?
About 215 million tons of solid garbage.

How many mammals lay eggs and nurse their young on milk?
Two — the duck-billed platypus and the echidna.

How deadly is the box jellyfish?

Its sting can kill a human in 3 minutes.

How many dimples are there on a regulation golf ball?

336.

How many parts of the baby's body did Rosemary Clooney look at in her search for its dimple, according to her song?

On the baby's knuckle, on the baby's knees
Where will the baby's dimple be?
Baby's cheek or baby's chin
Seems to me it would be a sin
If it's always covered by a safety pin
Where will the dimple be?

How did Henkel Dusseldorf help clean up the world?

Back in 1907 he invented the first household detergent, Persil.

How old is the world's oldest bank note?

Going on for 146 years old — the first bank note was issued by the Bank of Stockholm in 1661.

How many miles will a human being have walked in a lifetime?

By the age of 85 most people will have walked about 100,000 miles.

How long is the earth's longest glacier?

320 miles long — it's the Lambert-Fisher glacier in Antarctica.

How many stars are visible on a perfectly clear evening?

About 2,500.

How much area could be covered by human skin?

If it was spread out, the skin from an adult would cover about 7 square feet/2 square meters.

How much of the human body is water?

About 75%.

How many earth tremors are there on average every year?

About a million.

How much of the earth is covered by desert?

A seventh.

How quickly do young giraffes grow?

An inch a month.

How many calories do the Irish consume on average a day?

At 3,952 calories per person, per day, Ireland consumes more than any other nation.

How much of the earth's fresh water flows down the Amazon?

15%.

How long did the 1990s Gulf War last?

About 7 months — hostilities began on August 2, 1990 and Operation Desert Storm began withdrawing American troops on March 10, 1991.

How fast is Warp Factor 1 on Star Trek's Enterprise?

670,610,000 mph.

How much of the body's energy goes into feeding the brain?
20%.

How many brains does the silkworm moth have?
11.

How many bubbles are there in a bottle of champagne?
Over 25 million.

How many people still try to contact Shakespeare's Juliet?
Romeo and Juliet was set in the Italian city of Verona and every year about 1,000 letters arrive, addressed to Juliet, on Valentine's Day.

How old was Juliet when she met Romeo?
13.

How many Middle East countries don't have a desert?
Just the one — Lebanon.

How many times did John McEnroe win the men's title at Wimbledon?

Three — 1981, 1983 and 1984.

How many times did Pete Sampras win the men's title at Wimbledon?

Seven — 1993, 1994, 1995, 1997, 1998, 1999 and 2000.

How many times did Andre Agassi win the men's title at Wimbledon?

Once — 1992.

How many times did Chris Evert win the US Open tennis tournament?

Six — 1975, 1976, 1977, 1978, 1980 and 1982.

How many terms can an American President serve?

Two.

How many kinds of mollusks are found on dry land?

Only 2 — the snail and the slug.

How many times was Napoleon married?

Twice — his first wife, Josephine, was unable to provide him with an heir so he divorced her and married Archduchess Marie Louise of Austria.

How many terms can a British Prime Minister serve?

As many has he/she can win at an election.

How many strands of hair are there on Tweety Pie's head?

Three.

How old was President JF Kennedy when Marilyn Monroe sang Happy Birthday, Mr President to him?

He was celebrating his forty-fifth birthday.

How did Napoleon die?

Arsenic poisoning.

How long is the human DNA sequence?

3 billion bases long.

How many main blood types are there?

Types A, B, AB and O — each type is either Rh positive or negative.

How much of the human body is made up of blood?

About 8%.

How many volcanoes are there under the earth's seas?

About 10,000. There are only about 1500 on land.

How many species of carnivorous plants are there?

About 600 — insects are the usual victims but some can eat frogs, birds and small monkeys.

How fast is the crack of a whip?

At least 760 miles/475km per hour — its characteristic crack comes because it travels faster than the speed of sound, just like when a plane goes through the sound barrier.

How did Maxwell House coffee get its name?

It was named after the Nashville hotel where the original blend was served in 1886.

How did cappuccino get its name?
Its color resembled the robes of the order of Capuchin monks.

How many people died of the influenza epidemic of 1918?
20 million.

How much food is harvested every year from the ocean?
About 4 million tons.

How many stars are there on the Chinese flag?
Five.

How long does it take to grow a cultivated pearl?
Up to 2 years.

How many shark attacks are there every year?
On average, about 100 — of these 10 may result in a fatality.

How many time zones are there in the US?

Eight:
  Atlantic Standard Time (AST)
  Eastern Standard Time (EST)
  Central Standard Time (CST)
  Mountain Standard Time (MST)
  Pacific Standard Time (PST)
  Alaskan Standard Time (AST)
  Hawaii-Aleutian Standard Time (HST)
  Samoa Standard Time (UTC-11)

How did ancient Mayans try to please their rain god?

By throwing women into wells.

How many different types of metals are there?

86.

How many time zones are there in Australia?

Three:
  Eastern Standard Time (AEST)
  Central Standard Time (ACST)
  Western Standard Time (AWST)

How many active geysers are there?

About 700 worldwide — 300 of them are in Yellowstone National Park in Wyoming.

How often does the famous Old Faithful geyser in Yellowstone Park erupt?

About once every 76 minutes. It shoots out between 830 and 1885 gallons of water each time.

How long did Anne Frank manage to keep hidden from the Nazis during World War II?

25 months.

How old was Anne Frank when she died of Typhus in a concentration camp?

15.

How many people can start a riot?

According to dictionary definitions, the minimum number of people it takes to start a riot is three.

How many languages has Anne Frank's Diary been translated into?

67.

How many time zones are there in China?

One.

How much tea is there in the average tea bag?

2 grams.

How many toes does a cuckoo have?

Eight — four on each foot.

How many of Emily Dickinson's 1700 poems were published in her lifetime?

Seven.

How many Concorde aircraft were built?

16.

How high can bamboo grow?

Up to 130 feet.

How did the perfume Chanel No. 5 get its name?

Five was Coco Chanel's favorite number and she launched the perfume on the fifth day of the fifth month — 05/05/1921.

How can gold lessen the pain?

Gold salts are sometimes injected into muscles to relieve arthritis.

How many years did it take to make the first million Ford cars?

Seven.

How is one of Saturn's moons connected to New Year's Day?

January is named for the Roman god Janus and Janus is one of Neptune's moons.

How much do Americans love coffee?

They drink about 138 billion cups of coffee every year.

How many continents don't have a desert?
Only one — Europe.

How many crocuses does it take to make one ounce of saffron?
About 4,000.

How long does it take the cork tree to grow one layer of cork?
10 years.

How much do the numbers from 1-100 make when added consecutively?
5050.

How do butterflies taste the flowers they land on?
Through their back feet.

How would you scare a pogonophobic?
Grow a beard — pogonophobia is a fear of beards.

How stupid are jellyfish?
Jellyfish are 97% water and have no brains but they can tell dark from light and sense any movement around them,

How is a tittle better known?
A tittle is the dot over the letter 'i'. It is technically called a diacritical mark.

How many falling leaves does the oak tree lose in the fall (autumn)?
A mature oak will drop some 700,000 leaves.

How long does it take an oak tree to produce acorns?
As long as 30 years.

How many different languages are spoken in Indonesia?
About 365.

How many bones are there in the human head?
22.

How much can a baby elephant weigh?
A newly-born elephant can weigh up to 260 pounds.

How many teaspoons make a tablespoon?
Three.

How many teaspoons make a cup?
48.

How did the Red Sea get its color?
Sometimes it had large blooms of algae which, when dead, turned the sea's normal blue color red.

How was being born with a crooked nose fortunate in ancient Rome?
Those born with a crooked nose were said to have leadership qualities. No need for cosmetic surgery in ancient Rome, then.

How many different brands of beer are there?
More than 20,000.

How did the term 'cop' originate?

It comes from constable on patrol.

How many words in the English language don't rhyme?

Four — there are no rhymes for month, purple, orange and silver.

How many eyes do bees have?

Five — three small eyes on the top of its head plus 2 larger eyes at the front.

How much does a bushel of apples weigh?

About 42 pounds.

How many nuclear bombs have been lost at sea?

As of now, it is known that 92 bombs are out there in the ocean somewhere.

How many islands does Finland have?

179, 584.

How big is the actual summit of Mount Everest?
About the size of a pool table.

How many cases of spontaneous human combustion have been recorded?
More than 300.

How tall was Joseph Stalin?
5ft 4in/163cm.

How many times was Adolf Hitler married?
Once — he married his long-time companion Eva Braun shortly before his death.

How did Winston Churchill become an American?
In 1963 he became the first person to be awarded honorary citizenship of the United States.

How many churches did Sir Christopher Wren build in London?
As well as building St Paul's Cathedral, he built another fifty-one, between 1670 and 1711.

How prevalent are headaches?

Pretty widespread, given that over fifty billion aspirin tablets are taken every year.

How do crickets chirp?

They rub their wings together.

How tall can a cactus grow?

A saguaro cactus can grow more than 60 feet/18 meters and live as long as 300 years.

How long does the average hurricane last?

It generally takes 10 days from it starting to it blowing itself out.

How fast can a cold front travel?

30 mph — it can even overtake a warm front.

How would you use an aglet?

To tie the laces on your shoe. That's what the plastic bits on the end of the lace are called.

How do mosquitoes get the blues?

They probably don't, but they are more attracted to the color blue than to any other color.

How many pieces of wood make a violin?

About 70.

How many kinds of wood are perfect components of a violin?

For really good resonance the back is made of maple and the top of spruce.

How many sisters did Joey Tribbiani from Friends have?

Seven: Gina, Dina, Mary Angela, Mary Theresa, Cookie, Veronica and Tina.

How did Chandler Bing earn a living in the first few series of Friends?

He was a data processor.

How many of his Friends did Chandler hire with less than positive results?

Two — he hired Phoebe and Joey.

How did the term 'the graveyard shift' originate?

In Victorian times there was such a fear of being buried alive that when someone died, a small hole was left open between the casket and the surface. A string was tied around the dead person's finger which was attached to a bell that was hung above ground. If someone was buried alive they could ring the bell and whoever was on duty would dig them up. Someone was on duty 24 hours of the day and this was called the graveyard shift.

How many groups of instruments make up an orchestra?

Four — woodwind, percussion, strings and brass.

How many string instruments are generally in an orchestra?

Four — violin, viola, cello and double bass.

How long is the world's longest concert scheduled to last?

A performance of a piece of music by the experimental American composer John Cage, called organ2/ASLSP, started in an abandoned Church in Germany on September 5, 2001 and is scheduled to last until 2369. A clue to the length of the work is in the title organ2/ASLSP, with the letters standing for As SLow aS Possible.

How short is the shortest opera?

The Deliverance of Theseus, by Darius Milhaud lasts for seven minutes.

How many Americans get bitten by dogs every year?
About a million.

How many years did it take to build the Great Wall of China?
1700.

How many text messages are sent in the UK every month?
Over a billion.

How much of the gold used in the US is by dentists?
15% — for teeth, fillings and bridgework.

How many names were in the first ever telephone book?
50 — it was published in New Haven, Connecticut, in 1878.

How long do human fingernails grow in a year?
About 2.5in/6cm.

How far can a seal swim under water?
Up to 7 miles without coming to the surface.

How fast does sound travel?
In air it travels at about 1,100 feet per second. Sound waves travel about five times faster in water than in air.

How can you tell if a watermelon is ripe?
Knock and if it sounds hollow, it is ripe.

How can a frog be hypnotized?
If it's laid on its back and its stomach gently stroked.

How many hummingbirds does it take to weigh one ounce?
18 (of the tiniest species).

How cold is it for hypothermia to be fatal?
If the body cools down to about 80 degrees F/27 degrees C.

How did the authorities in 18th century Europe show their disapproval of published books?

They whipped them.

How long ago is there evidence of shoemaking?

10,000 BC — there is evidence of Ancient Egyptians wearing sandals and pictures of Native Americans having left and right shoes.

How many people in the US were slaves at the beginning of the 19th century?

20% of the total population.

How many Irish went to America when Ireland suffered its great Potato Famine?

Between 1846 and 1856 some 2 million Irish immigrants arrived in the US.

How were people punished in ancient Egypt for killing a cat?

They were put to death.

How many different animal shapes are there in Animal Crackers?

18 — the lion, elephant, bison, tiger, cougar, camel, rhinoceros, kangaroo, hippopotamus, hyena, zebra, sheep, bear, gorilla, monkey seal, giraffe and koala.

How did the people of Nicaragua think they could protect themselves against an erupting volcano?

By throwing beautiful young women into the mouth of the volcano.

How were people punished in Turkey in the 16th and 17th centuries for drinking coffee?

By the death penalty.

How long ago was the first ever police force set up?

1667 — in Paris.

How long ago was the earliest recorded case of kicking the smoking habit?

On the 5th April 1679, Johan Katsu, Sheriff of Turku in Finland, wrote in his diary: "I quit smoking tobacco." He died one month later.

How long ago was income tax introduced in England?
1799 — by British PM William Pitt.

How many years of peace have there been in the civilized world in the last 3,500 years?
230.

How many Native Americans were killed by the Spaniards within 20 years of Columbus discovering the New World?
1.5 million.

How much pressure is the human body under at sea level?
Every portion of the body is subjected to an air pressure of 14.7 pounds per square inch.

How did pirates think they could improve their eyesight?
By wearing an earring.

How long was the shortest recorded war?
30 minutes — it was between Zanzibar and England in 1896.

How far do athletes run in the marathon?

26.2 miles (42.2 km).

How many land mines were dug up from the banks of Suez Canal after the 1973 war between Egypt and Israel?

Nearly 700,000.

How long was a day 500 million years ago?

20.6 hours.

How was the Sword of Damascus strengthened?

It was plunged into a flame.

How did Vikings make use of the skulls of their enemies?

They used them as drinking vessels.

How many countries were involved in World War II?

57.

How often is a car stolen in the US?
Every 30 seconds.

How many more women shoplift than men?
The ratio is four women to one man.

How long did the longest recorded kiss last?
130 hours and 2 minutes.

How many people are killed per year by vending machines falling on them?
On average, an unlucky 13.

How many Americans think that Elvis is still alive?
7%.

How many Americans claim to have talked to the devil personally?
About 7%.

How many babies are born worldwide every minute?
About 200.

How many Americans claim to have been abducted by aliens?
About 3 million.

How many people died in the Stalinist purges in the Soviet Union?
About 30 million.

How many statues of Joan of Arc are there in France?
About 40,000.

How much saliva does the average person produce in a lifetime?
About 25,000 quarts — enough to fill two swimming pools.

How many Americans are involved in accidents with their jewelry per week?
About 800.

How many lands did Gulliver travel to?
Eight:
  Lilliput
  Brobdingnag
  Laputa
  Balnibarbi
  Luggnagg
  Glubbdubdrib
  Japan
  Land of the Houyhnhns

How long would it take to drive a car to the sun?
About 150 years.

How many calories in a Big Mac?
493.

How many calories in celery?
About 17 — although it takes more calories to eat a stick of celery.

How old are English newspaper crossword puzzles?
The first appeared in 1924 in the Sunday Express.

How many teeth does the average human adult have?

32 — 28 plus 4 wisdom teeth.

How many different categories of icebergs are there?

Six:

  Growler

  Bergy Bit

  Small

  Medium

  Large

  Very Large

How many knights were there around King Arthur's Round Table?

According to Dryden, there were twelve. Sir Walter Scott named 16 but there are definitely 10 accepted by most authorities:

  Lancelot

  Tristram

  Lamorack

  Tor

  Galahad

  Gawain

  Palomides

  Kay

  Mark

  Mordred

How many people did Charles Manson kill in the notorious La Bianca/Sharon Tate murders?

He did not actually physically murder anyone. He ordered his followers Susan Atkins, Patricia Krenwinkel, Leslie Van Huten and Charles 'Tex' Watson to carry out the killings.

How many Apostles were there?

13. Simon (Peter), Andrew, James, John, Philip, Bartholomew, Thomas Didymus, Matthew, James, Thaddeus, Simon the Zealot, Judas Iscariot, Matthias.

How many books are there in the Bible?

66.

How many books are there in the Old Testament?

39.

How many Gospels are there in the Bible?

Four — Matthew, Mark, Luke and John.

How many different kinds of human teeth are there?

Four — incisors, canines, premolars and molars.

How many atmospheric layers does the earth have?

Four — the troposphere, stratosphere, mesosphere and ionosphere.

How many Ivy League universities are there?

Eight:

Brown

Columbia

Cornell

Dartmouth

Harvard

Pennsylvania

Princeton

Yale

How long was Michael Jackson's video for Thriller?

14 minutes.

How many types of classical column are there?

Five:

Doric

Ionic

Corinthian

Tuscan

Composite

How many countries have won the soccer World Cup?

Seven:

England

Germany (as West Germany in 1974)

Brazil

Argentina

Italy

France

Uruguay

How many people are injured in Britain during the Guy Fawkes celebrations in November of each year?

More than 1,000.

How much did the most expensive music video cost?

In excess of $7 million. It was Michael Jackson's Scream.

How is a car with a manual shift more economical than an automatic?

A manual shift vehicle gets 2 miles more per gallon than an automatic.

How many people die in the US every year in car crashes?

Over 43,000.

How many copies of Michael Jackson's Thriller album were sold worldwide?

More than 59 million copies.

How many records need to be sold to go platinum?

According to the British Phonographic Industry:

Singles

Silver – 200,000

Gold – 400,000

Platinum – 600,000

Albums

Silver – 60,000

Gold – 100,000

Platinum – 300,000

According to the Recording Industry Association of America:

Singles

Silver – 500,000

Gold – 1,000,000

Platinum – 10,000,000

Albums

Silver – 500,000

Gold – 1,000,000

Platinum – 10,000,000

How many people in the US die every year in falls (off ladders, down stairs, off buses)?

Nearly 15,000.

How keen are the Japanese on comics?
About 20% of all publications in Japan are comic books.

How many directors were there for Gone with the Wind?
Five:
 Victor Fleming
 Sam Wood
 William Cameron Menzies
 George Cukor
 B. Reeves Eason

How is the last working day of the week bad for banking?
50% of all bank robberies take place on a Friday.

How many faces did Joanne Woodward show Eve to have for her Academy Award winning role?
The Three Faces of Eve.

How much can a polar bear weigh?
The average male adult bear weighs between 850 and 900 pounds. One was killed back in the 1960s which weighed 2,210 pounds.

How many kinds of light can a goldfish see?

The goldfish is the only animal able to see both infrared and ultraviolet light.

How many post offices are there in India?

Over 152,792 post offices. In the United States there are about 38,000.

How much is a ton of money?

One million dollars in $1 notes weighs about a ton.

How did Peter the Great of Russia tax his subjects?

He put a tax on beards. That certainly was an incentive for shaving.

How many deadly sins are there?

Seven:

Pride

Greed

Lust

Envy

Gluttony

Wrath (anger)

Sloth (laziness)

How much peanut butter is consumed in the US every year?
800,000,000 pounds.

How much more spinach did Americans eat after Popeye came on the scene in 1931?
Spinach consumption increased by 33%.

How can a beard tell time?
When a man has 5 o'clock shadow.

How many eyes does the night have?
According to the hit song by Bobby Vee, The Night has a Thousand Eyes.

How many days did Teri Hatcher and Charlize Theron spend in the Valley in 1996?
They co-starred in the film Two Days in the Valley.

How is Mickey Mouse known in Italy?
Topolino.

How does Spongebob Squarepants make a living?

He is a fry cook at the Krusty Krab.

How many teenagers were chosen to be the original Mighty Morphin Power Ranges?

Five — Jason, Kimberly, Billy, Zack and Trini.

How would you recognize the winner of the Miss Bogen County Contest?

Miss Piggy was the winner.

How many points does Kermit the Frog have around his neck?

11.

How did Kermit get his name?

He was named after Jim Henson's childhood friend, Kermit Scott.

How did Kermit get his big break in show business?

He started out on Sesame Street as a reporter, interviewing nursery rhyme characters.

How many brothers and sisters did Kermit have?
On an edition of Extreme Makeover: Home Edition Kermit said that he had 3,265 brothers and sisters. He was referring to tadpoles.

How does Miss Piggy display her displeasure with Kermit?
She karate chops him.

How did Bert and Ernie from the Muppets get their names?
They were allegedly named after the policeman and the cab driver in Frank Capra's classic film, It's a Wonderful Life, starring James Stewart.

How many Academy Awards did James Stewart win?
One — for The Philadelphia Story.

How many films did James Stewart make with director Alfred Hitchcock?
Four:
 Rear Window
 Rope
 The Man Who Knew Too Much
 Vertigo

How many Best Director Academy Awards did Alfred Hitchcock win?
He was nominated four times, for Lifeboat, Spellbound, Psycho and Rear Window, but never won.

How did the group The Engaged Couples become better known?
They renamed themselves ABBA.

How many stars surround the mountain in the Paramount Pictures logo?
22.

How many lawyers are there in the US?
In 1995 the number of lawyers was 896,000. It is estimated that there are now about one million lawyers. Since 1970 the number of lawyers has doubled from one lawyer per 700 people to about one lawyer per 300 people. The US has seventy percent of the world's lawyers and only five percent of the world's population.

How is Brad's drink better known?
Pepsi-Cola — two of its important ingredients were pepsin and kola nuts.

How many M&Ms are sold in the US every day?
About 200 million.

How many people were tried as witches or wizards in the Salem Witch hunts of the 1600s?
More than 150 — 20 died.

How old was Mary Shelley when she wrote Frankenstein?
19.

How is a prestidigitator better known?
As a magician.

How is a dactylogram known to the police?
It is a fingerprint.

How is the Book of Esther unique in the Bible?
It is the only book not to mention God by name.

How many English words end in 'ous'?

Four:

tremendous

horrendous

stupendous

hazardous

How many of the world's capital cities begin with O?

Three — Oslo in Norway, Ottawa in Canada and Oubadougou in Burkina Faso.

How long ago was writing not punctuated?

Punctuation didn't begin to appear until the 15th Century.

How did the universal symbol of pawnbroking, the three balls, originate?

The legend has it that one of the Medici family slew a giant with three sacks of rocks and that three symbols — the sacks became balls in this case and were incorporated into the Medici family crest. As the Medici family were important moneylenders at the time, the three balls became synonymous with moneylending.

How is the Land of Rabbits better known?

Spain.

How many of Shakespeare's plays feature ghosts?

Four:

Julius Caesar

Richard III

Hamlet

Macbeth

How many copies of Moby Dick did Herman Melville sell during his lifetime?

50.

How does poor man's thermometer register temperature?

Tree crickets are so known because heat affects their activity. Listen to how many chirps they make in 15 seconds then add 37. This will give a fair indication of the temperature outside.

How long will it be before the next year that can be written upside down and be the same?

6009.

How does a hamlet differ from a village?

A hamlet is a village without a church.

How is Rio de Janeiro always running at the start of each year?
Rio de Janeiro translates as River of January.

How long would it take to count to one million if each number took one second to count?
About 12 days.

How is the IDEO locator easily recognized?
It is the 'You Are Here' arrow.

How did Queen Isabella of Spain finance Columbus' voyage to America?
She pawned the Crown Jewels.

How did dinosaurs walk the earth?
On their toes, supposedly.

How many times are gemstones are mentioned in the Bible?
There are more than 1,700 references to gems and precious stones.

How fast is a polar bear?

Polar bears can run at 25mph/40kph and jump 6ft/2m in the air.

How much water can a baobab tree store?

Up to 25,000 gallons.

How many land animals cry like humans?

One — the elephant.

How far into the air did the first rocket reach?

In 1926 Robert Goddard fired a rocket reaching a height of 40 feet/12 meters.

How was 7-Up named?

The drink came in a 7-ounce container and Up was the way the bubble floated.

How fast is the earth spinning on its axis at the equator?

It spins at about 1,038 mph or 1,670 kilometers an hour.

How much is lightning to blame for bush fires?
90% of fires are started by people. Lightning accounts for less than 10%.

How many areas of the body lack hair follicles?
Two — the soles of the feet and the palms of the hands.

How would someone with heterochromia be easily recognizable?
They would have two different color eyes.

How would coconut oil affect a diet?
Badly. It has 91 percent, by weight, saturated fat. More than butter or lard.

How dangerous are hippos?
Hippos are known to have killed more than 400 people in Africa, more than any other animal.

How much ice cream does the average American consume in a year?
21 liters. In Britain the consumption is 8 liters per person.

How many Beatles have there been since the group started?
Six — John Lennon, Paul McCartney, George Harrison, Ringo Starr plus Stu Sutcliffe and Pete Best.

How many of Snow White's dwarves had beards?
Six. Only Dopey didn't sport face whiskers.

How many fiddlers did Old King Cole call for?
Three:
  Old King Cole was a merry old soul,
  And a merry old soul was he.
  He called for his pipe, and he called for his bowl,
  And he called for his fiddlers three.

How did the expression crocodile tears come to mean fake tears?
The crocodile sometimes secrete a fluid from their eyes when they catch prey. When they're happy that is.

How much does a ten-gallon hat hold?
About 3/4 gallon.

How many blackbirds were baked in a pie?

24 — according to the nursery rhyme:
  Sing a song of sixpence a pocketful of rye,
  Four and twenty blackbirds baked in a pie...

How many American babies are named after relatives?

60%.

How many movies are produced by Bollywood each year?

About 1000 — twice the number as Hollywood.

How many troops did the Grand Old Duke of York march up the hill, and down again?

The Grand Old Duke of York, he had ten thousand men.

How many cars took part in the 2005 US Grand Prix at Indianapolis Motor Speedway?

Six — disputes about the resurfaced track led all but three teams to refuse to race after the parade lap. All these teams were using Michelin tires. The remaining teams using Bridgestone tires were left to compete and the winner was Michael Schumacher driving a Ferrari.

How old was the oldest man when he died?

Shigechiyo Izumi died of pneumonia in Japan at the age of 120 years and 237 days.

How old was Shirley Temple when she retired from the screen?

21 — she was born in 1928 and left Hollywood in 1949.

How many steps are there to heaven?

Three — according to the Eddie Cochran song:

  Step one — you find a girl you love.

  Step two — she falls in love with you.

  Step three — you kiss and hold her tightly.

  Yeah! That sure feels like heaven to me.

How many bags of wool were supplied in the nursery rhyme Baa Baa black sheep?

Three — one for the master, one for the dame and one for the little boy that lives down the lane.

How did Elizabeth Taylor dial up an Oscar?

She won an Academy Award for her role in Butterfield 8.

How did Alfred Hitchcock telephone for a killing?
He directed Dial M for Murder.

How many days was Robert Redford on the run as the Condor?
Redford starred in Three Days of The Condor (1975).

How close to Tulsa was Gene Pitney?
24 Hours from Tulsa was the title of a Pitney hit record.

How many Pillars of Wisdom did Lawrence of Arabia write about?
The Seven Pillars of Wisdom is an autobiographical account of T.E. Lawrence's experiences in Arabia fighting against the Turks between 1916–1918.

How many careers has Barbie had?
Over 80. Among them, an astronaut, doctor, teacher, marine, pilot, dancer and actress.

How old is Mickey Mouse?
The first appearance by Mickey Mouse was in Steamboat Willie, in 1928.

How many of the ancient world's seven great wonders survive?

One — the Great Pyramid of Giza.

The other six were:

The Hanging Gardens of Babylon

The giant statue of Zeus at Olympia

The temple of Artemis at Ephesus

The Mausoleum of Halicarnassus

The Colossus of Rhodes

The Lighthouse of Alexandria

How much older is Barbie than Ken?

One year — Barbie burst onto the public stage in 1959. Ken made his debut in 1960. They met at a photo-shoot in 1961.

How did the expression 'on a wing and a prayer' originate?

The phrase comes from a World War II song written by Harold Adamson in 1943. It was based on the actual words of the pilot of a damaged plane as he spoke to the control tower: Tho' there's one motor gone, we can still carry on, Comin' in on a wing and a prayer.

How long were Barbie and Ken together before they decided to spend more time with other friends?

43 years.

How many countries buy Barbie?

More than 150.

How much does the world's most expensive Barbie cost?

Diamond Barbie, a one-off creation to celebrate her 40th birthday in 1999, had a price tag of 85,000 US dollars, or approximately £50,000. The diamond firm De Beers made sure that diamonds were definitely Barbie's best friend, with a dress sporting 160 diamonds plus other items of jewelry.

How did Bambi change species?

In the original story by Felix Salten he was a roe deer, while in the Disney film he was a white-tailed deer.

How many famous detectives did Agatha Christie create?

Her two most famous sleuths are Hercule Poirot and Miss Marple.

How many copies of Agatha Christie novels have been sold?

More than two billion — she is the best selling author of all time.

How did Poirot throw off his mortal coil?

He died peacefully in his sleep on the 6th of August 1975, while staying at Styles, the location where he first appeared in print in the Mysterious Affair at Styles in 1920.

How many acting Baldwin brothers are there?

Five — Alec, Daniel, Joseph, Stephen and William.

How many Barrymore stars are there on the Hollywood Walk of Fame?

Six — Drew Barrymore, Ethel Barrymore, John Barrymore, John Drew Barrymore and Lionel Barrymore. Lionel has two stars, one for film and one for radio.

How does the male platypus protect his turf?

He has spurs on his hind feet which release venom. The venom renders opponents paralyzed and can kill small animals. It causes excruciating pain to humans but is not deadly.

How did the Incas measure the passage of time?

By how long it took a potato to cook.

How many tons of grapes does it take to make one ton of raisins?
Four.

How far does the average banana travel before it is peeled?
Around 4,000 miles.

How many tins of Spam are opened worldwide every minute?
15.

How would you play with a bandalore?
The bandalore was the original name for a yo-yo.

How was the original yo-yo used?
In the Philippines, a form of yo-yo was used for hunting

How many verses are there in the Greek National Anthem?
158.

How much wire does it take to make a slinky?

63 feet (about 19 meters).

How many paintings did Vincent Van Gogh sell in his lifetime?

Out of 900 paintings and 1100 drawings, he sold only one painting titled Red Vineyard at Arles for 400 Francs.

How many official languages are used by the United Nations?

Six.

Arabic

Chinese

English

French

Russian

Spanish

How many horses are there in the world?

About seventy five million.

How many crayons can be made from one acre of soya?

80,000.

How did the phrase 'often a bridesmaid, but never a bride' originate?
It was coined for a Listerine mouthwash advert in 1928.

How many Mr Potatoheads have been sold since they reached the shelves in 1952?
More than 50 million.

How much of the world's salt is used to de-ice American roads?
More than 10%.

How many questions does the average four-year old child ask per day?
Over 400.

How long does the average person spend on the phone in a lifetime?
About two years.

How many husbands tell their wives daily that they love them?
20% — and how many mean it?!!

How long will the average person spend in their lifetime waiting for traffic lights to change?

About two weeks.

How many name changes has St Petersburg had?

Its name was changed from St Petersburg (1703) to Petrograd (1914), then to Leningrad (1924) and then back to St Petersburg (1991).

How many countries were the principal opponents in World War II?

Six:

United States

Great Britain

France

Soviet Union

Japan

Italy

Germany

How many people drowned when the German vessel Wilhelm Gustloff was sunk by a Soviet submarine in 1945?

More than 7,700. It is the greatest sea disaster of modern times.

How long does the average person spend in the shower?

12 minutes.

How many people perished in Hitler's siege of Leningrad?

800,000 out of total population of 3 million.

How many of her own brothers did Cleopatra marry?

Two — Ptolemy XIII and Ptolemy XIV.

How many famous Romans courted Cleopatra?

Two — Julius Caesar and Mark Antony.

How did ancient Egyptians pay their taxes?

In honey.

How long did it take to prepare an Egyptian mummy?

Up to 70 days.

How long was the average bandage length used on an Egyptian mummy?

1.5 miles/2.5km.

How many islands are there in Japan?

3,900.

How many ships were said to have been sunk by a quick stare from Helen of Troy?

None — she was said to have a face that 'launched' a thousand ships.

How long does one year on Neptune last?

165 Earth years.

How many tenpin skittles need to be knocked down for a strike?

Ten.

How many children were in Enid Blyton's Famous Five?

Four — Georgina, Julian, Dick and Anne. The fifth member is Timmy the dog.

How many miles of public roads are there in the US?
Four million miles.

How many miles of public roads are there in the UK?
About 230,000.

How many of the ill-fated Edsel automobiles were sold before manufacture was discontinued?
Just short of 112, 000.

How much did an ebay bidder pay for a piece of Britney Spears' gum?
$263.

How many whiskers does the average cat have?
24.

How many peanuts go into a pound of peanut butter?
About 720.

How many kinds of tomatoes are there?
Over 4,000.

How violent are the male yellow baboons of Tanzania?
A male baboon will be seriously injured by another baboon about once every six weeks.
It will take three weeks to recover and then it will be injured again. It's a tough life.

How many legs does a lobster have?
Eight.

How many claws does a lobster have?
Two.

How many players are there in an Aussie Rules football team?
Each team has 18 players on the oval at the one time.

How many players are there in a basketball team?
Each team has 5 players on the court at one time.

How many players are there in an American football team?

Each team has eleven players on the field at the one time. NFL teams usually have 53 players to choose from.

How many players are on a Gaelic football game?

Each team has 15 players.

How many notes are there in an octave?

Eight.

How is Maurice Micklewhite better known?

Michael Caine.

How is Reg Dwight better known?

Elton John.

How is Marion Morrison better known?

John Wayne.

How is Doris Mary Ann Von Kapplehoff better known?
Doris Day.

How is Frances Gumm better known?
Judy Garland.

How is Archibald Leach better known?
Cary Grant.

How is Richard Starkey better known?
Ringo Starr.

How was Old Ski Nose better known?
Bob Hope.

How many US Presidents did Bob Hope entertain?
11 — starting with Franklin Delano Roosevelt and ending with Bill Clinton.

How many Bob Hope stars are there on the Hollywood Walk of Fame?

Four — one each for Radio, TV, Movies and Live Theater.

How is Kathy Kane better known?

Batwoman.

How is Oswald Chesterfield Cobblepot better known?

Penguin, one of Batman's enemies.

How is Montgomery, Lord Falsworth, better known?

As Marvel Comic's Union Jack.

How is Barbara Gordon better known?

Batgirl — she was the daughter of James Gordon, the police commissioner of Gotham City.

How is the martial arts prodigy, Cassandra Cain, better known?

Batgirl (another one). She became Batman and Robins' protégé in the 1990s.

How long did Jesus of Nazareth spend in the desert?
40 days and 40 nights.

How many years did Moses and his followers spend in the wilderness?
40 years.

How is Lamont Cranston better known?
The Shadow.

How is Brian Braddock otherwise known?
He was another Marvel creation: Captain Britain.

How is Frank Castle, the marine deserter better known?
Punisher.

How is Private Steve Rogers better known?
Captain America.

How many lines are there in Shakespeare's sonnet number 99?

15:

The forward violet thus did I chide:

Sweet thief, whence didst thou steal thy sweet that smells,

If not from my love's breath? The purple pride

Which on thy soft cheek for complexion dwells

In my love's veins thou hast too grossly dyed.

The lily I condemned for thy hand,

And buds of marjoram had stol'n thy hair:

The roses fearfully on thorns did stand,

One blushing shame, another white despair;

A third, nor red nor white, had stol'n of both

And to his robbery had annex'd thy breath;

But, for his theft, in pride of all his growth

A vengeful canker eat him up to death.

More flowers I noted, yet I none could see.

How is Peter Parker better known?

Spiderman.

How is Bruce Banner better known?

The Hulk.

How many lines does a sonnet have?

14.

How is James Howlett better known?

He was born James Howlett but now goes by the name Logan, otherwise Wolverine in the X Men series.

How many permutations are there on the standard 3x3x3 Rubik's cube?

43, 252,003, 274,489,856,000.

How many sonnets are generally attributed to William Shakespeare?

154.

How many symbols are used in the Chinese zodiac?

12. Each signifies one 12-year cycle. They are:

Rat

Ox

Tiger

Rabbit

Dragon

Snake

Horse

Sheep

Monkey

Rooster

Dog

Boar

How many signs of the zodiac are there?

12:

Capricorn

Aquarius

Pisces

Aries

Taurus

Gemini

Cancer

Leo

Virgo

Libra

Scorpio

Sagittarius

How many fairy tales did the Brothers Grimm collect?

Some 200, plus 10 categorized as legends.

How old was Genghis Khan when he succeeded his father?

13.

How many years was Victoria Queen of England?

64.

How many prime ministers were in office during Queen Victoria's reign?
10.

How many Coca-Cola products are consumed every second worldwide?
Over 7,000.

How did the tomato change from a fruit to a vegetable?
In 1893 the US Supreme Court ruled in Nix vs Hedden that tomatoes were to be known as vegetables. The case was about paying tariffs according to whether imports were fruit or vegetables.

How did Coca-Cola first cross the Atlantic?
Aboard the German airship, Graf Zeppelin.

How would you make a Buck's Fizz?
The drink is a combination of champagne and orange juice. It is virtually the same as a Mimosa cocktail.

How is flour made self-raising?

It is generally a mixture of white flour and chemicals — baking soda and salt — which give self-rising qualities.

How many different shapes of pasta are there?

More than 600.

How long is the longest Coca-Cola truck?

The longest truck is in Sweden. It is 79ft/24m long.

How did tripolini (little bows) pasta get its name?

It was made to celebrate the Italian's conquest of Tripoli, a town in Libya, in 1911.

How many different colored grape varieties are there?

Eight — black, blue, blue-black, golden, red, green, purple and white.

How many kinds of rice can be driven?

Two — Toyota can mean 'bountiful rice field', while Honda translates as 'the main rice field'.

How many calories does an average-sized potato contain?

About 110. A cup of rice contains 225 calories while a similar measurement of pasta weighs in with 155 calories.

How long does it take for rice to grow?

105 days from planting to harvesting.

How much water does it take to grow one kilo of rice?

About 5,000 liters of water.

How much of the earth's population consumes rice?

Almost one half. That's about 3 billion people and counting.

How many people rely on rice for survival?

60% of the world's population.

How much pizza is eaten in the US every day?

About 100 acres a day, or 350 slices a second.

How many countries have Pizza Huts?
More than 90 countries.

How many months of the year are associated with eating oysters?
Traditionally oysters were only consumed in months including the letter 'r'. It was considered safe to eat oysters in January, February, March, April, September, October, November and December. In the Northern Hemisphere these were the months when the seas were coolest and oysters therefore contained less potentially harmful bacteria.

How else is the star Sirius known?
The Dog Star.

How many humps does a newborn camel have?
None.

How is the Hitchcock film, Rope, notable?
It was shot on a single location with very long takes so that it looked like it was one long take from beginning to end.

How many times does the word 'mafia' appear in The Godfather (1972)?
It doesn't. Evidently the Italian-American Civil Rights League came to an agreement with the film's producers that the term would not be used.

How many women, to date, have been nominated for Best Director Oscars?
Three:
  Lina Wertmüller for Seven Beauties (1976)
  Jane Campion for The Piano (1983)
  Sofia Coppola for Lost in Translation (2003).

How would myrmecology get you jumping?
It is the scientific study of ants.

How is the Pentateuch also known?
The first five books of the Old Testament:
Genesis, Exodus, Leviticus, Numbers and Deuteronomy.

How many cards are in a tarot pack?
78.

How did the term 'salary' originate?

The Romans used to pay their soldiers in salt and the term 'sal dare', meaning to give salt, became salary in English.

How do herons deal with mosquitoes?

By stamping and pecking — they go at the mosquitoes with their feet and beaks at a rate of about 3,000 steps and pecks an hour. This deals with about 80% of the threat from the blood-sucking varmints.

How old are moon rocks?

Rocks as old as 4.4 billion years old were collected from the moon during the Apollo program.

How did Italian wine merchants react to the introduction of coffee in the 1600s?

They asked the Pope Clementine VIII to ban it. He woke up, smelt the coffee and pronounced it a Christian drink.

How was Erich Weiss better known?

Harry Houdini.

How was the first European coffee marketed?
It was sold in pharmacies as a medicine.

How many coffee beans make an espresso?
About 42.

How long does it take for a human baby to grow, from conception to birth?
About 270 days.

How would a Chinese bride dress for her wedding?
Chinese brides wear red.

How big can the biggest flower grow?
The Rafflesia arnoldi flower can be as big as an umbrella.

How fast can bamboo grow?
Some varieties can grow 3ft/1m in a day.

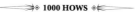

How many gold medals did Jesse Owens win at the Berlin Olympics of 1936?

Four — he won the 100 meters, the long jump, the 200 meters and was part of the American gold-winning 4 x 100 meters relay team.

How deadly is the Ebola virus?

It kills 4 out of 5 people it infects.

How long could the average home be powered by one bolt of lightning?

Two weeks, if it could be harnessed.

How fast are telephone signals?

Signals travel at 100,000 miles a second.

How many world records did Jesse Owens break in the space of 45 minutes in 1935?

Three — at a track meet in Ann Arbor, Michigan, Jesse Owen equaled the record for the 100 yards and broke the world records for the long jump, 220 yards and 220 yards hurdles.

How quickly can a Venus flytrap catch its prey?
It takes less than half a second to snap and close!

How many eggs a year will the average hen lay?
257.

How would you play with cystallite?
You'd cue it up. It's the material snooker balls are made from.

How many functions does the human liver perform?
More than 500, including storing vitamins and cleansing the blood.

How was sugar used in primitive medicine?
A paste made from white sugar granules and water was used on minor injuries such as scrapes and burns. The sugar cleansed the wound, helped speed up healing and reduced scarring.

How many odors can a human turn their nose up at?
People can differentiate about 10,000 different smells.

How many trees would have to be planted to offset the greenhouse emissions of a refrigerator?

72 trees.

How much carbon dioxide can an acre of trees remove from the atmosphere in a year?

26 tons.

How much of the world's communication is in English?

It is thought that up to three quarters of all mail and eighty percent of email is in English, but that will rapidly change once China and India get really hooked on the web and mobile phones.

How many plastic bags are used by Australians every year?

More than 6 billion — if tied together, they would stretch around the world 37 times.

How would you eat a fava bean?

According to Hannibal Lecter, with human liver and a nice Chianti to wash it down. The 6th Century BC philosopher Pythagoras banned the fava bean as he thought it contained the souls of the dead. The fava bean hasn't had good press.

How is Volney the lion better known?

He was the lion in the MGM logo. He lived at Memphis Zoo.

How deadly is the Black Mamba snake?

The mortality rate is over 95%.

How much shrimp is produced every year to satisfy our appetites?

Over 5 billion pounds. 20% of that is farmed shrimp.

Where is the shrimps' heart?

In its head.

How many people have died from road accidents since the introduction of the motorcar?

About 25 million.

How much water does a dairy cow drink in a day?

Up to 50 gallons — enough to fill a bathtub.

How would you navigate a pogonip?
With fog lamps — pogonip is a heavy winter fog containing ice crystals.

How many varieties of orchid produce anything edible?
One — out of 20,000 kinds of orchid, one produces the vanilla pod.

How many Amazon tribes have been wiped out in the last one hundred or so years?
120.

How far is the shortest scheduled air flight?
It is between Westray and Pap Westray in the Orkney Islands. The flight lasts for a minute and a half.

How is winter bad for the heart?
There are twice as many heart attacks in winter as in summer.

How many islands make up Venice?
117.

How did Patty and Mildred Hill leave their mark on annual celebrations across the world?

Back in the 1890s they changed the words of a song they'd written called Good Morning to All to Happy Birthday to You.

How many canals are there in Venice?

177.

How much more deadly than the male is the female Black Widow spider?

She can consume up to 20 males a day.

How many people die every year from eating puffer fish?

This expensive delicacy is popular in Japan, but the liver of the puffer fish is lethal. Even highly-trained chefs sometimes miss unseen traces of the liver and as many as a hundred people a year die from ingesting it.

How much is 'all the tea in China'?

Back in the 1970s the United Nations estimated it at about 356,000 tons. That's a lot of tea bags.

How much of Russia is covered by forest?

A quarter.

How fast is the housefly?

The average fly cruises at about 5m an hour.

How much did the first Kodak Brownie camera sell for in 1900?

$1 — it was marketed to kids because of its easy use.

How many languages spell TAXI the same way?

13:

English
French
German
Swedish
Spanish
Danish
Norwegian
Dutch
Czech
Slovak
Hungarian
Romanian
Portuguese

How do pearls disappear?
They melt in vinegar.

How many parts are there to a cow's stomach?
Four — the rumen, the recticulum (storage area), the omasum (for water absorption) and the abomasums (the only one with digestive juices).

How did the month of May boost the Anglo-Saxons' calcium levels?
May was known as Thrimilce, or the month in which cows could be milked 3 times a day.

How many US Presidents were born on the 4th of July?
One — Calvin Coolidge was born on the 4th of July 1872. He served from 1923 to 1929.

How much are the highest opening scores in Scrabble?
Russian peasants will net you 128 points (MUZJIKS) while QUARTZY or SQUEEZY both score 126 points.

How many moons does Mars have?
Two — Phobos and Deimos.

How did Willy Loman make his living in Arthur Miller's Death of a Salesman?

He sold ladies' hosiery.

How many species of mosquitoes are there?

Over 3000 — 165 different species live in the US.

How is yak's milk noticeably different to cows milk?

Yak's milk has a pink hue.

How far does the earth's magnetic pull stretch into space?

Over 37,000 miles.

How much of San Francisco was destroyed in the great Earthquake of 1906?

500 blocks of the city were destroyed and around 700 people lost their lives.

How many Japanese cities were bombed with an atomic bomb?

Two — Hiroshima and Nagasaki.

How much of the earth's topsoil is lost every year?

About 7%, estimates suggest.

How long does it take Mars to orbit the sun?

Two Earth years.

How cold does it get on Mars?

-81 degrees F/-63 degrees C.

How quickly does Mercury orbit the sun?

Once every 88 days — faster than any other planet.

How many children comprised the world's largest family?

A Russian woman, known only as the wife of Feodor Vassilyev from the village of Shuya, gave birth to 69 children in the 18th century during 27 pregnancies. The matriarch produced 16 pairs of twins, seven sets of triplets and four quadruplets.

How safe is the bicycle?

It is apparently the most dangerous form of transport.

How long does it take a blood cell to circulate through the human body?
60 seconds.

How many human chromosomes are there?
48 — peas have 14 and crayfish 200.

How many balls are used to pick the winning numbers in the British National Lottery?
Seven.

How lethal is the Colombian poison-arrow frog?
It has enough poison to kill 1,000 humans.

How long did Coca-Cola contain cocaine?
18 years. 1885–1903.

How many beaches are there in Australia?
Over 7,000. More than any other country.

How was Mars portrayed in ancient Greece?

Mars was portrayed as the god of war. He was a warrior in full battle armor with a crested helmet and carrying a shield.

How does the Monarch butterfly make itself poisonous?

It eats the milkwood plant. When a bird eats one of the butterflies, it becomes sick and soon learns to avoid that particular species.

How old is a male gorilla when he turns into a Silverback?

The hair covering a mature male gorilla changes color between the ages of 10 and 12.

How often can a cat have a litter of kittens?

A cat can have a litter of 3–7 kittens every 4 months.

How much typing (in touch typing) does the left hand do?

About 56%.

How big was the largest known kidney stone?

1.36 kilos/3 pounds.

How long does a taste bud last?

On average, 10 days.

How did 'Mary had a little lamb' kickstart the music recording industry?

They were the first words said by Thomas Edison over the phonograph.

How many breaths does the average human take in a year?

About 10 million.

How many eyes does a scallop have?

35 — all blue.

How stretched can a human's nerves get?

There are about 47 miles of nerves in the body. That's a long stretch.

How many breeds of dog can't bark?

Only one — the African wolf dog, or Basenji.

How many hours of sleep does a newborn baby cause its parents to lose?

Between 450 and 700 hours of sleep in the first year of the child's life.

How many American families own a dog?

About a third.

How far can the average human walk using the energy from one pound of fat?

Almost 30 miles. That's about 48 km.

How many chemicals make up salt?

Two — it is 60% chloride and 40% sodium.

How many innings are there in a baseball game?

Nine.

How does Steve McQueen try to make his Great Escape?

He steals a motorcycle and heads for the hills. He, like most of the 76 escapees, is recaptured.

How does Dorothy escape the Wicked Witch of the West in the Wizard of Oz?
Dorothy throws a bucket of water over her and she melts.

How did Terriers earn their keep down on the farm?
They were used as rat catchers and to rid barns and stables of vermin.

How many ways do sharks have their young?
Three — some sharks lay eggs in the water. Some sharks keep their eggs inside them until they hatch. Other sharks grow baby sharks inside them like humans do.

How many feet in a mile?
5,280 feet.

How many species of marsupials live in Australia?
About 120, including kangaroos, Tasmanian devils, wombats and koalas.

How many species of marsupials live in the US?
One — the Virginia opossum.

How many sons did Walt Disney have?

None. He had two daughters, one of whom was adopted.

How many colors are there on a Rubik's cube?

Red, orange, yellow, green, blue and white.

How did the term 'fall guy' originate?

In the movies the stuntman is the fall guy because he takes the fall for the actor.

How did the term 'one for the road' come to mean a drink before going home?

On their way to be hanged at Tyburn Tree in London, convicted felons would be allowed to have a last drink — or a few — at pubs along the route from prison to the place of their execution.

How did England come to be known as a nation of shopkeepers?

Napoleon famously used the phrase to describe the lack of readiness for war with France, saying they were too busy trading to notice the danger they were in.

How long is a 'jiffy'?

A jiffy is a unit of time equal to 100th of a second.

How can you differentiate between a fresh egg and a stale egg?

A fresh egg sinks in water, a stale egg floats.

How did the phrase 'close, but no cigar' originate?

Cigars used to be given as prizes in fairground contests, so, when a player missed out on a prize the barker would use the phrase.

How many species of penguin are there?

17 — they all live in the Southern Hemisphere.

How old was the youngest person ever to be elected US President?

At 43 John F. Kennedy was the youngest to be elected. The youngest President inaugurated was Theodore Roosevelt who was 42 when he took office after the assassination of William McKinley.

How many US States start with an M?
Eight:
 Maine
 Maryland
 Massachusetts
 Michigan
 Minnesota
 Mississippi
 Missouri
 Montana

How many US Presidents had fathers who were clergymen?
Three — Chester Arthur, Grover Cleveland and Woodrow Wilson.

How many seeds are on an average strawberry?
200.

How long is the Statute of Liberty's finger?
8 feet/2.5 meters long — its fingernail measures 13 by 10 inches/33 by 25cm.

How many kinds of living birds are there that can't fly?
15 — the smallest is the Inaccessible Island Rail, the largest is the Ostrich.

How many rocking chairs did President Jimmy Carter bring with him to the White House?

Five.

How old was George Foreman when he won the World Heavyweight Boxing title in 1994?

44 — he became the oldest person to ever win the title.

How many trombones led the big parade?

According to the Music Man, 76 trombones led the parade.

How many cornets followed the trombones in The Big Parade?

110 — the lyrics say 'With a hundred ten cornets close at hand.'

How do strawberries differ from all other berries?

They are the only variety to carry their seeds on the outside.

How long does it take an ostrich to hatch?

42 days.

How many plagues were inflicted on ancient Egypt, according to the story of Moses and the Israelites?

10:

1. Water turned to blood
2. Frogs
3. Gnats or lice
4. Flies
5. Livestock became diseased
6. Boils
7. Hail mixed with fire
8. Locusts
9. Darkness
10. Death of firstborn

How many ways did Paul Simon suggest it was possible to leave your lover?

The song title is 50 Ways to Leave Your Lover, but Simon only gives five clear ways:

Slip out the back, Jack.

Make a new plan, Stan.

You don't need to be coy, Roy.

Hop on the bus, Gus.

Just drop off the key, Lee, and get yourself free.

What happened to the other forty-five?

How did French tobacconists used to keep their tobacco from drying out?

They put a carrot in each bin.

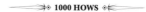

How heavy was the heaviest dog on record?
Zorba, an Old English Mastiff, weighed in at 156 kilos/343 pounds and measured
8 feet 3 inches/2.5 meters from head to tail. He battles it out with another Mastiff whose
disputed weight is 159 kilos.

How many colors can carrots be?
Five — orange, purple, white, red and yellow.

How does Bugs Bunny's diet differ from his wild cousins?
Wild rabbits do not eat carrots.

How fast is air expelled when you cough?
Up to 60mph/97kph.

How many trees can a beaver cut down in one year?
As many as 200.

How noisy is a pig?
The average pig squeals at between 100 and 115 decibels.

How fast does a hedgehog's heart beat?
On average the heart beats 190 times a minute. This slows to 20 beats a minute during hibernation.

How many eggs are laid by an American oyster in a year?
On average, about 500 million. Only one little egg will reach maturity.

How infested is the human body with bacteria?
Every square inch of the human body has an average of 32 million bacteria on it.

How much skin does a human shed every hour?
About 600,000 particles. By the age of 70 a person will have shed 105 pounds of skin.

How many words, on average, does a woman say every day?
7,000 words — men manage around about 2,000. That's where the strong silent type comes from.

How many couples get married in Las Vegas every day?
On average, 150 tie the knot.

How did Reno come to be known as the divorce capital of the US?
A quickie divorce could be done in six weeks. That was the minimum stay required in Nevada to get a divorce.

How is lead not lead?
The lead in pencils is actually graphite, not lead.

How much did Joe Shuster and Jerry Siegel sell all rights to the comic-strip character Superman for in 1938?
$130.

How many quills does a porcupine have?
About 30,000 quills.

How far can you draw with a pencil?
The average pencil will draw a line 35 miles long or write 50,000 English words.

How many words are there in the average person's vocabulary?
Between 5,000–6,000 words.

How many types of surfaces is tennis played on?

Three — grass, clay and hard court. Hard court can be anything from concrete to especially manufactured 'carpet'.

How long did it take Hitchcock to film the famous shower scene in Psycho?

Seven days.

How many Oscars was Walt Disney nominated for?

64.

How many tennis balls are used during Wimbledon fortnight?

About 42,000 balls.

How many Oscars did Walt Disney collect between 1931 and 1969?

35.

How many syllables are there in a haiku?

17.

How did the bell in the Houses of Parliament clock tower in London come to be called Big Ben?

Some say it got its nickname from the champion boxer of the time, Ben Caunt. It is more likely that it was named for a rather large gentleman named Sir Benjamin Hall who was Commissioner for Works at the time of its building and whose name is inscribed on the bell.

How many years would a couple have been married if they received diamonds for their anniversary?

50 years.

How many years would a couple have been married if they received pearls for their anniversary?

30 years.

How many years would a couple have been married if they received china for their anniversary?

20 years.

How many years would a couple have been married if they received paper for their anniversary?

One year.

How old was the oldest man to receive a Winter Olympics medal?
83-year-old Norwegian-American Anders Haughen received a bronze medal for his ski jump 50 years after he had competed in 1924. The reason Anders had to wait so long to receive his award was an error which had occurred in the scoring system, and it wasn't until 1974 that it was discovered.

How can you tell the age of a fish?
One way to tell the age of a fish is by looking at its scales. Like trees they have growth rings, called circuli. Clusters of them are called annuli. Each annulus represents one year.

How high can human tonsils bounce?
Higher than a rubber ball of similar size and weight but only for the first half an hour after they have been removed.

How is a banana tree not a tree?
The banana tree isn't really a tree but a herb.

How many volts are in a lightning bolt striking the earth?
Up to a 100 million.

How many gallons of water are there in a cubic mile of fog?

Less than one.

How long does it take an oil tanker fully loaded to stop?

20 minutes.

How many times brighter is a full moon than a half moon?

Nine times brighter.

How many times does The Lord's Prayer appear in The Bible?

Twice — once in Matthew VI and again in Luke XI.

How many gallons of fuel are there in a jumbo jet when it takes off?

4000 gallons.

How are the Aurora Australis also known?

They are the Southern Lights as opposed to the Aurora Borealis or Northern Lights.

How fast does a raindrop fall?
7mph/11kph.

How big is a standard grave?
7'8 x 3'2 x 6' or 2.3m x 96cm x 1.8m

How fast must windspeed be to be called a hurricane?
74mph/119kph.

How many cars are junked in the US every year?
About 7 million.

How heavy is sunlight?
If you weigh all the sunlight that hits the earth at the same time it weighs about the same as an ocean liner.

How many faces does an enneahedron have?
Nine.

How many thunderstorms are there in progress at any one time in the earth's atmosphere?
About 1800.

How fast does a molecule of air travel?
About the speed of a shooting bullet.

How many bacteria are in a single drop of liquid?
About 50 million.

How fast can bamboo grow?
About 3 feet/90cm a day.

How fast is earth traveling through space?
660,000mph/1,056,000kph.

How long would it take to count all the stars in the sky?
About 3000 years at the rate of one per second.

How did penknives get their name?

Long before the age of Biros, people used to carry a small knife around with them to sharpen the goose quills which were used back then for writing.

How much water is stored in a camel's hump?

None — the humps are made up of fat and flesh which helps them survive when there's no food and water available.

How many colors are there in a rainbow?

Seven — red, orange, yellow, green, blue, indigo and violet.

How many Olympic medals did Johnny Weissmuller win before Hollywood cast him as Tarzan?

Five — at the Paris Olympics of 1924 he won gold in the 100 meters freestyle, 200 meters freestyle and as part of the US 4x200 meters freestyle relay team. He also won a bronze medal as part of the US water polo team. At the Amsterdam Olympics (1928) he won the 100 meters freestyle gold.

How many summer Olympics have been canceled?

Three — 1916, 1940 and 1944 Olympics, due to world wars.

How many times has the US played host to the Summer Olympics?

Four:

1904 — St Louis

1932 — Los Angeles

1984 — Los Angeles

1996 — Atlanta

How many Olympic sports using a ball were played in 2004?

Twelve:

Baseball

Basketball

Beach Volleyball

Football (soccer)

Handball

Hockey

Rhythmic gymnastics (balls, hoops and ribbons are used)

Softball

Tennis

Table tennis

Volleyball

Water polo

How many kinds of wrestling were there in the 2004 Olympic Games?

Two — Greco-Roman and Freestyle.

What is the shortest distance run in an Olympic track and field event?

60 meters in the competition for the women's Heptathlon.

How many events comprise Equestrian events in the Olympics?

Three — dressage, eventing and show jumping.

How many different boxing weights are there in the Olympic Games?

Eleven:

  Light Flyweight
  Flyweight
  Bantamweight
  Featherweight
  Lightweight
  Light Welterweight
  Welterweight
  Middleweight
  Light Heavyweight
  Heavyweight
  Super Heavyweight

How was Wilhelm II of Germany known to his less than reverent subjects?

Stupid Willy.

How many events are there in the Olympic Heptathlon?
Seven:
  100m hurdles
  High jump
  Shotput
  200 meters
  Long jump
  Javelin
  800 meters

How is Edward Charles Stuart better known?
Bonnie Prince Charlie.

How is Louis XIV of France best remembered?
The Sun King.

How was President Bill Clinton referred to by the Secret Service?
Elvis was his code name.

How did Snow White's seven dwarfs make a living?
They were miners.

How many children did US President John Tyler have?
15 — there may also have been other children born out of marriage. He had the most children of any president before and after.

How did President Reagan get the nickname 'The Gipper'?
In Knute Rockne, All American (1940) he played a character named George 'The Gipper' Gipp.

How many members were there in the 1960s Rat Pack?
Five:
 Frank Sinatra
 Dean Martin
 Sammy Davis Jr
 Peter Lawford
 Joey Bishop

How many cities were unable to hold their allocated Olympic Games because of war?
Four — the 1916 Berlin Olympics were canceled because of the Great War 1914–1918. In 1940 Tokyo was meant to host the games but The Olympic Committee canceled their participation because of the outbreak of the Second Sino-Japanese War. The games were given to Helsinki, but these also had to be canceled because of the war in Europe. The same reason accounts for why the 1944 Olympics in London were canceled.

How many legs does a millipede have?
It most definitely doesn't have one thousand. Estimates range from a few hundred to a maximum of 750.

How many people did Noah take onto the Ark?
Seven plus himself.

How many rings are there on the Olympic flag?
Five — one for each continent — blue, yellow, black, green and red.

How many official languages do the Swiss speak?
Four — German, French, Italian and Romansch.

How many numbers are there in the US police code for homicide?
Three — the code is 187.

How many Indians did Agatha Christie write about?
Ten Little Indians.

How many steps were there in the classic Alfred Hitchcock thriller about World War II espionage?

39 Steps.

How far did Bruce Willis have to take Mos Def in their 2006 police drama?

16 Blocks.

How many 'angels' did Charlie employ?

Six — Kate Jackson, Farrah Fawcett (Majors), Jaclyn Smith, Cheryl Ladd, Shelley Hack and Tanya Roberts.

How would you play Octopush?

It's also known as the game of underwater hockey

How many first dates did Adam Sandler and Drew Barrymore have in their 2004 hit comedy?

50 First Dates.

How many candles did Molly Ringwald blow out in 1984?

Sixteen Candles — although her parents forgot her birthday so not much of a celebration.

How many accomplices did Danny Ocean have in Ocean's Eleven?

Ten — between them they were planning to rob three Las Vegas casinos.

How many years did the US have prohibition?

13 (1920–1933).

How many actresses have played Emma Peel in the Avengers?

Two — Diana Rigg in the TV series, Uma Thurman in the 1998 film version.

How far did Matthew Perry go to betray a gangster played by Bruce Willis?

The Whole Nine Yards (2000).

How many weeks did Kim Basinger and Mickey Rourke spend together in 1986?

Nine and a half weeks.

How far did Eminem go in his feature film debut?
Eight Mile — the miles refer to the city limits of Detroit.

How many days did it take to lose a guy, according to Kate Hudson and Matthew McConaughey?
They co-stared in How toLlose a Guy in 10 Days (2003).

How many Model T Fords were built?
15,700,003.

How many languages has the rules of Monopoly been translated into?
27.

How long did the longest recorded game of Monopoly last?
70 days.

How much did the first three-minute telephone call between New York and London cost in 1927?
$75.

How many men were out in the 1988 film based on the 1919 World Series match when the White Sox accepted bribes to throw the series?
The film was called Eight Men Out.

How long is the average orbit of Halley's comet?
76 years — it is due to be seen again from earth in 2062.

How many bishops are there on a chessboard?
Four — two black, two white.

How many pawns are there in a chess set?
16 — 8 black, 8 white.

How many times has Polo been played at the Olympic Games?
Five — In 1900, 1908, 1920, 1924 and 1936.

How many throwing events are there in Olympic track and field?
Four — discus, hammer, shot and javelin.

How often does a lioness have cubs?
Every two years she will give birth to between two and four cubs.

How many 'Qs' are there in a game of Scrabble?
One.

How many self-portraits did Rembrandt paint?
More than 50.

How does the city of Pamplona celebrate the Fiesta of San Fermín?
By running bulls through the streets. This is extremely dangerous for the youths that try and outrun the bulls. At least 14 have been killed and hundreds injured.

How old is Lisa in The Simpsons?
Eight years old.

How old is Bart in The Simpsons?
Ten years old.

How do the cities of Nice (France), Cologne (Germany), Rio de Janeiro (Brazil) and New Orleans celebrate Shrove Tuesday?
With Mardi Gras.

How many nephews does Donald Duck have?
Three — Huey, Dewey and Louie.

How did the owl and the pussycat travel in Edward Lear's children's tale?
The Owl and the Pussycat went to sea in a beautiful pea green boat.

How did Peter Pan keep one step ahead of the crocodile?
The crocodile had swallowed a clock and wherever he went it went tick tock, tick tock.

How many ghosts did Scrooge see in A Christmas Carol, by Charles Dickens?
Four:
Jacob Marley – his business partner.
The Ghost of Christmas Past.
The Ghost of Christmas Present.
The Ghost of Christmas Yet to Come.

How did the term 'nerd' come into being?

It was used by Dr Seuss in his 1950 book, If I Ran the Zoo.

How many kernels are there on the average cob of corn?

800 — arranged in 16 rows.

How many times a year does the average person blink?

84 million times.

How many people died in the Great Fire of London?

There are only six recorded deaths although there may have been many more – but six is an incredibly small number for a fire of such magnitude.

How would you tell time in Las Vegas?

You'd have to wear a watch as there are no clocks in casinos.

How is nylon transatlantic?

It is an acronym for New York and London.

How much of London burned down in the great Fire of 1666?
About 50%.

How long did it take to put out the Great Fire of London?
Four days.

How many people died in the Great Plague of London in 1865?
The official list contains 68,576 names but the total is probably closer to 100,000.

How many wheels does the longest limousine have?
26 — the body length is about 100ft/30m long.

How many feature films had Brandon Routh appeared in before he pulled on the big S in Superman Returns?
None — he had appeared in a number of TV shows but had never starred in a film.

How did Delilah rob Samson of his strength?
She cut off his hair.

How long after canned food had been introduced was the can opener invented?

About 30 years. Initially the cans were used for soldiers' rations. They opened the cans with their bayonets.

How did SPAM get its name?

It is said to be a syllabic abbreviation of SPiced hAM. The person who thought of the new name for Hormel Spiced Ham was said to be paid $100.

How were houses designated plague houses?

They were marked with a red cross on their doors. Many doors were nailed shut to prevent entering or leaving the houses.

How many British prime ministers have been assassinated?

One — Spencer Percival was shot dead in the lobby of the House of Commons on May 11, 1812, by John Bellingham, a merchant who had lost money in Russia. When the government refused to compensate him for his losses, he took his revenge on the PM.

How many US presidents were bachelors during their term of office?

One — James Buchanan — president from 1857-61.

**How many brothers and sisters did Holden Caulfield
have in The Catcher in the Rye?**

Holden had a younger sister, Phoebe, an older brother, D.B. and a younger brother, Allie,
who died of leukemia.

How many British prime ministers had American mothers?

Three:

The Duke of Grafton (1767–70)

Winston Churchill (1940–1945 and 1951–55)

Harold Macmillan (1957–63)

How do the French celebrate the beginning of the French Revolution?

Bastille Day, July 14, commemorates the day in 1789 when the people stormed the Bastille
and released the seven prisoners who were kept there.

**How do the British celebrate the plot to blow up the House of
Parliament and King James the First of England?**

The attempt was foiled on November 5, 1605, and on that date fires are lit, fireworks are
set off and effigies of Guy Fawkes, the leader of the potential bombers, are burned.

How many Rocky Balboa movies are there?

Five — Rocky, Rocky II, Rocky III, Rocky IV and Rocky Balboa — in production 2006.

How many days a year does the average person sleep?

Approximately 122 days are spent sleeping.

How does Eleven Plus Two equal Twelve Plus One?

Eleven Plus Two is an anagram of Twelve Plus One.

How many Marx Brothers were there?

Five — Chico, Groucho, Gummo, Harpo and Zeppo.

How many mammals suffer from sunburn?

Humans and pigs are the main sufferers although mammals with pale fur are prone as well.

How would you identify a purple finch?

By its crimson plumage.

How many steps lead up to Sherlock Holmes' apartment at 221B Baker Street?

17.

How many US presidents were sworn in without using the Bible?
One — Theodore Roosevelt.

How long does the average man's beard grow in a month?
Half an inch, just over a centimetre.

How many muscles do we use to speak?
72 muscles are used to speak just one word.

How many children did Queen Victoria have?
Nine.

How is Norville Rogers of 224 Maple Street, Coolsville, better known?
He's Shaggy from Scooby Doo.

How many Horsemen of the Apocalypse are there?
Four — they are traditionally said to represent War, Famine, Pestilence and Death.

How would an albatross affect a round of golf?

It would be great! An albatross is when a hole is played in 3 less strokes than par. i.e. if a hole has a par of 5 and a player only takes 2 strokes to complete the hole he/she would score an albatross.

How many female pharaohs of Egypt were there?

Three:
  Hatshepsut (15th century BC)
  Nefertiti (14th century BC)
  Cleopatra (69–30 BC)

How many creatures make up a griffin?

A griffin is a mythical creature with the head and wings of an eagle, the body of a lion (or tiger), front feet with talons and the tail of a scorpion. Humans flew on them.

How many heads did the Hydra that was slain by Hercules have?

The hydra was a nine-headed snake.

How many heads did Cerberus, the dog guarding the Greek Underworld, have?

Three.

How many mice did Cinderella's fairy godmother turn into horses to pull the coach taking her to the ball?

Six.

How many soldiers did Ulysses take with him in the wooden horse that brought down Troy?

19.

How many victims did the notorious Victorian murderer Jack the Ripper kill?

Five for certain. There has been speculation that as many as 18 women were butchered by the Ripper but the only 5 confirmed victims were Mary Ann Nichols, Annie Chapman, Elizabeth Stride, Catherine Eddowes and Mary Jane Kelly, all killed between 31st August, 1888 and 9th November 1888.

How did Vlad Tepes of Transylvania, the inspiration behind the Dracula myth, dispose of his victims?

Over the years he has come to be known as Vlad the Impaler. He murdered thousands of his subjects by forcing wooden stakes through their bodies. He also burned people alive, mutilated them, tied them up in forests where they would be attacked by wild animals, strangled them and had nails knocked into their heads. The fictional Dracula isn't half as scary or violent as his source of inspiration.

How many cases of murder was the doctor Harold Shipman tried and convicted of?
15 sample cases — it is thought that he killed as many 250 elderly patients.

How many arms and tentacles does a squid have?
Eight arms like an octopus plus two tentacles which they use to grab their prey.

How do squids move?
By jet propulsion — they squirt water out of a tube and therefore rapidly move in the opposite direction.

How many paper bags can be produced from a twenty-year-old tree?
700.

How long does alcohol stay in the human system?
Up to 12 hours after a person has stopped drinking.

How long is the shortest intercontinental flight?
20 minutes – it goes between Gibraltar and Tangier, a distance of 34 miles.

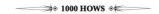

How many tons of pollutants are released into the earth's atmosphere every year?
Over a billion.

How many orchid seeds weigh as much as one grain of wheat?
30,000.

How much of the world's gold is found in South Africa?
Over two-thirds.

How many colors of stars are there?
Two – red stars give off cool light and blue stars give off hot light.

How were early lasers measured?
They were measured by the amount of blue razor blades they could puncture – called Gillettes.

How many languages are spoken in Africa?
More than 800 — many of them are local dialects spoken by less than 100,000 people

How did the Saudi Arabian government of 1976 plan to irrigate their desert sands?

They hired a French firm to look into the feasibility of bringing huge icebergs to the country and dumping them in the desert.

How many major deserts are there in North America?

Four:
  The Chihuahuan
  Sonoran
  Mojave
  Great Basin

How many countries are there in Africa?

In 2006 — 55.

How fast can glass break?

3000mph/4800kph.

How long was Peter Mustafic of Botovo, Yugoslavia silent for?

Forty years. Back in 1920 he became mute as a way of getting out of doing military service. He claimed to have become used to being silent and didn't speak again until he had turned 90.

How big was the largest recorded tiger?

The heaviest tiger on record was a Siberian Tiger, weighing 1,025 lbs.

How much of the world's fresh water can be found in Lake Baikal, in southern Siberia?

20% — it is the world's largest freshwater lake and it provides 90% of Russia's fresh water.

How many sub-species of tigers have been hunted to extinction in the last one hundred years?

Three — the Bali tiger disappeared in the 1940s, the Caspian Tiger in the 1970s and in the 1980s man eliminated the Javan Tiger!

How many astronauts manned each Apollo flight?

Three.

How many events of the original ancient Greek pentathlon are still included in the modern pentathlon?

One — the original events were discus, javelin, long jump, foot race and wrestling. The only surviving sport is running. The other events making up the modern pentathlon are pistol shooting, fencing, swimming and riding.

How much food did Charles Lindbergh carry with him on his record-breaking transatlantic flight?

Four sandwiches.

How many sports are there where a team has to move backwards to win?

At least two – rowing and tug of war.

How much money do Americans spend on golf balls each year?

Over 630 million dollars.

How fast was the fastest round of golf ever played?

A whole round of 18 holes was played in 9 minutes and 28 seconds in Tatnuck CC in Worcester on 9 September 1996.

How many golf courses are there in the US?

Over 10,000.

How many new golf holes are built every day across the world?

About 12.

How many golf balls are still on the moon?

Three.

How fast do professional hockey players skate?

20–25mph/32–40kph.

How many men have won the Wimbledon Singles tournament 4 times in a row?

Three:

Bjorn Borg, Pete Sampras, Roger Federer

How did the explorer and writer Thor Heyerdahl travel from Peru to Polynesia?

On a balsa wood raft. He wanted to prove that South Americans could have traveled and settled in the Polynesian islands.

How many children took the Willy Wonka tour of the Chocolate Factory?

Five:

Charlie Bucket, Veruca Salt, Augustus Gloop, Violet Beuragarde, Mike Teavee.

How fast can a freestyle swimmer swim?

About 4mph/6.5kph.

How much was a 200-year piece of Tibetan cheese auctioned off for in 1993?

$1,513.

How many countries make up the axis of evil, as defined by president George W. Bush?

Three — Iraq, Iran and North Korea.

How many horns does a unicorn have?

A single horn.

'How's that?' is a term used in which sport?

Cricket. It's what the players shout when they think a batsman has got himself out.

How many Bibles are sold every minute worldwide?

About 50.

How many eyes did a cyclops have?

These giants of mythology had one large eye in the center of their foreheads.

How many sides has the Pentagon, in Washington?

Five — it has seven floors, five above ground and two below.

How many survivors were there of the Titanic disaster?

Estimates suggest between 705 and 713. Many bodies were never recovered.

How many teeth does a slug have?

Approximately 27,000.

How many legs has a Daddy Longlegs?

Eight — sometimes they can grow up to 30 times the size of its body.

How do wasps sleep?

Wasps have been seen to bite into the stem of a plant and actually lock their jaws in tight, then stretch out at right angles to the stem and fall asleep with legs dangling.

How many kinds of the 500 species of Eucalyptus will koalas eat?

Just six —they're very picky eaters.

How old is the oldest known living tree?

Called Methuselah, this pine in California is said to be over 4,700 years old. Its exact location is kept secret for its protection.

How many species of life are there on Earth?

About ten million.

How many time zones are there on Earth?

24.

How many wives did the world's greatest lover have?

King Mongut of Siam had more than 9,000 wives. He said he only loved the first 700.

How many times has England failed to qualify for the World Cup Football tournament?

Three — 1974, 1978 and 1994.

How many forms of travel use the nautical mile as a distance measurement?

Two — sea and air travel.

How many times has da Vinci's Mona Lisa been stolen?

Once — in 1911. It was handed back to officials in Italy in 1913 and was back on display in 1914.

How many enclaved countries are there, i.e. situated within the borders of other countries?

Three:

The republic of San Marino, enclaved within Italy

Vatican City, within the city of Rome, in Italy

The Kingdom of Lesotho, embedded inside South Africa

How many Mona Lisas are there?

Four — under the painting currently on view x-rays show da Vinci painted three versions before he was happy with the final portrait.

How many times has Australia played in the World Cup soccer finals?

Twice — 1974 and 2006.

How long is a marathon?

The marathon is a long-distance road running event of 26 miles 385 yd/over 42 km. The name 'marathon' comes from the legend of Pheidippides, a Greek soldier who was dispatched from the town of Marathon to Athens to announce that the Persians had been miraculously defeated in the Battle of Marathon. It is said that he ran the entire distance without stopping, but moments after proclaiming his message to the city, he collapsed dead.

How long is the longest commute in the world?

Chris McKee lives in Dunedin, New Zealand and travels 12,000 miles/20,000 km to work as a police officer in London, England. Luckily for him, he has some flexibility in his job as he works 2 weeks of 12 hour shifts then gets 2 weeks off.

How long is the world's longest escalator?

The longest escalator in the western hemisphere is located at the Wheaton station of the Washington Metro subway system. It has an overall length of 508 feet/155 meters and takes over 3 minutes to ride.

How far above sea level is the highest capital city in the world?

La Paz, the administrative capital of Bolivia is the highest, at 11,913 feet above sea level. Before Tibet was invaded by China, Lhasa was a capital city which stood 12,087 feet above sea level.

How many countries does the Andes Range of Mountains run through?

Five:

Columbia

Ecuador

Peru

Bolivia

Chile

How many times has the United States played in the World Cup soccer finals?

Eight — 1930, 1935,1950, 1990, 1994, 1998, 2002 and 2006.

How many countries speak English?

According to the British Council, more than 75 countries have English as their official or special status language. More than 2 billion people speak English as their first or second language.

How tall was the tallest recorded man?

8ft 11.5in/2.7 meters — Robert Wadlow of Alton, Illinois was known as the Boy Giant. He died from an infection when he was 22.

How many commandments are there?

Ten:

1. I am the LORD your God who brought you out of the land of Egypt, from the house of slavery. Thou shalt have no other gods before Me.

2. Do not make a sculpted image or any likeness of what is in the heavens above.

3. Thou shalt not swear falsely by the name of the LORD.

4. Remember the Sabbath day and keep it holy.

5. Thou shalt honour your father and your mother.

6. Thou shalt not murder.

7. Thou shalt not commit adultery.

8. Thou shalt not steal.

9. Thou shalt not bear false witness against your neighbor.

10. Thou shalt not covet your neighbor's house.

How much was a Medieval Groat worth?

Four old pence.

Fin